101 School
Assembly Stories

101 School Assembly Stories

by Frank Carr

LONDON
W. FOULSHAM & CO. LIMITED
NEW YORK TORONTO CAPE TOWN SYDNEY

W. FOULSHAM & CO. LIMITED
Yeovil Road, Slough, Berks., England

ISBN 0–572–00857–0

© Copyright by S. Carney 1973

Art work © W. Foulsham & Co. Ltd. 1973

Printed in Great Britain by
Redwood Burn Limited, Trowbridge & Esher

Contents

Acknowledgement

I am very grateful to Mr. Edward Coe, deputy headmaster of Conway J. and I. School, Birmingham for much sound advice and many fruitful suggestions.

TRUE STORIES

Johnny Appleseed

One day those who lived on the banks of the river saw a strange sight. Down the Ohio drifted a boat made from two canoes tied together. Both canoes were almost full of rotting apples. The boat with its peculiar cargo was paddled by a young man of about twenty-five, dressed in the rough, comfortable clothes of the American outdoor man of those days. This was their first sight of Johnny Appleseed.

Of course Appleseed was not his real name: it was Chapman. He was born – no one is quite sure where – pretty close to the year in which the Americans broke away from Britain and began to run their own country. We know little about his childhood except that he used to run away from home every now and again to live for a time among the rivers and forests which he loved from his earliest days.

As a young man he left the big cities of the eastern part of the United States and moved out to what came to be known as the Wild West. On the way he picked up a large quantity of apples which had been used for making cider. These apples, or rather their seeds, could be used to plant orchards in the wide open lands to the west. This, then, was the Johnny Appleseed the farmers saw drifting down the river.

He went ahead and planted his apple

seeds. As he had plenty left after this he travelled around the district carefully burying the seeds where he was most hopeful that they would take root. He enjoyed helping farmers who were having difficulty with their trees, for it soon turned out that he had a love for and knowledge of plants that those experienced settlers could not match. It was not long before he was known all over the West as an expert plant doctor.

Farmers worried by plant diseases used to send for Johnny Appleseed and the young man travelled hundreds of miles to use his healing skill.

Soon stories began to gather around the name of the strange man who dressed like Robinson Crusoe. It was said that he went off on long journeys all over the United States in order to plant apple trees. It was known that he scattered healing herbs so that they would spread and be useful in a part of the country where doctors were few and far between. People saw that he was kind to all animals, even the snakes that bit him.

Johnny Appleseed was a religious man. His favourite books were the Bible and works by saintly men. One day a visiting preacher said in the village church, 'Who nowadays behaves like those early Christians? Who now even looks like an early Christian?' There was a cry of 'I do,' and up stood Johnny Appleseed in his tattered trousers, shirt made out of an old sack and hat that had started life as a saucepan.

The Indians of those parts looked on him as a great medicine-man and none attempted to harm him in his wanderings, although most of them bitterly hated the white men who had driven them from their rich hunting grounds. The white settlers once learned that the Indians were about to attack their homes.

It was essential that someone should ride to the soldiers' camp to bring troops. Johnny Appleseed rode all through the night, stopping only at lonely farms to warn of the coming danger. It is said, though no one knows whether it is true or not, that in the war which followed he travelled over a wide area, warning Americans of approaching trouble.

Johnny Appleseed lived to about seventy-two. He died of pneumonia, caught while on a long trip to repair damage to an orchard. All Americans were sad at his passing, for he had lived a gentle life in those harsh times. While others had destroyed life he had encouraged and increased it.

The Corporal and the Officer

Two hundred years ago the United States of America were still ruled by Britain. Many of the folk who lived there were descended from people who had gone over from the British Isles. At last the Americans became dissatisfied with the way the British were running things and decided to rule their own country. This could only lead to war. The British sent over a well-trained army to bring the Americans, whom they called rebels, back under their rule.

The Americans raised an army to defend their new freedom. As commander-in-chief they appointed a man named George Washington. He led his troops, many of them farmers who had never fired a gun in anger, with great skill, but at first the war went very badly for the Americans. They were forced to spend a lot of time avoiding battle with the experienced British troops.

One day a corporal in the American army told his men that they must fell some trees in order to make a bridge. They set to work willingly but there were so few of them that the work came along very slowly. The corporal stood by and gave orders. He directed his soldiers this way and that, but he did not lend a hand with the chopping and carrying.

A uniformed officer rode up and watched the scene for a few minutes. Then he said to the corporal, "You haven't enough men for this job, have you?"

"No, sir," answered the corporal. "We could do with a lot of help."

"Then why don't you pitch in and give a hand yourself?" asked the officer.

"What!" said the other, "I'm a corporal, sir. It wouldn't be right for me to roll up my sleeves with the ordinary soldiers. I have a position to keep up."

"Of course," said the officer. Then he got off his horse, took off his jacket, rolled up his sleeves and set to work with the soldiers. He showed himself to be as fit as the youngest of them. In a short time the task was finished.

As he rode away the officer said, "Corporal, when you have another tough job and you need more men please send for the commander-in-chief and I will come again." It was George Washington.

No doubt he left the corporal thinking that in future he would never feel himself too important to do the little jobs that must be done.

Florence Nightingale

Long ago a war broke out between Britain and France on one side and Russia on the other in a place called the Crimea. Reports began to come back to Britain of dreadful conditions in the army hospitals. "Something must be done," the newspapers shouted, to take better care of soldiers wounded while fighting. Everyone became so angry that the government decided to send a band of nurses to help. It was led by a woman named Florence Nightingale.

She was thirty-four years old, handsome, lively and strong-minded. She had been born into a well-off family who expected her to live the easy life of a lady of those times. She refused this comfortable way of living, preferring to take up nursing. When war broke out she was the matron of a hospital. All her spare time was spent studying how hospitals were run, writing angry letters and newspaper articles in which she called for better treatment in them and trying to make people see that the country needed a hospital service run by trained nurses.

Florence jumped at the chance to serve in the Crimea. She gathered thirty-eight nurses, some of them Anglican and Catholic nuns, and set off for an army hospital in Turkey. She was distressed by what she found there. The hospital – really an army barracks – was overcrowded and damp.

Most of its five thousand patients were suffering not from wounds but from cold, starvation and disease. The few doctors were unable to cope with the growing numbers of wounded, the piles of paper-work, the shortage of supplies and the cramped conditions. Soldiers were dying of harmless wounds which a little care could easily cure. Dirt was everywhere.

Florence Nightingale set to work. She and her nurses, often working twenty hours a day, quickly put an end to the disorder. They began by cleaning the place from end to end. They improved the food, the bed-clothes, the medicines and – above all – the nursing. Florence opened another ward to relieve the overcrowding. She completely changed the running of the hospital.

You must not think that all this happened smoothly; it did not. She had to fight, write, threaten, scold and bully nurses, doctors, army officers, journalists and politicians to get her way. Florence Nightingale soon found herself accused by those she worked with of being crazy for power, bossy and more interested in running things in a business-like way than in curing her patients. It hurt her to hear these things but it did not stop her from carrying on.

The soldiers adored her. She soon became known as " the Lady with the Lamp ", for she used to tour the wards every night, lamp in hand, to see that all the men were comfortable. The sick and wounded soldiers knew that she worked only for them. They saw the changes in food, clothing and treatment. They felt themselves get better every day from wounds which, a short time before, would have killed them. They knew whom they had to thank.

Florence Nightingale spent the rest of the war working with all her energies. Her band of nurses was joined by many more. She visited the battle area, caught fever and spent weeks in bed, weak and helpless. When she got on her feet again her health was never the same. But ill-health never stopped her from driving herself to the limits of her strength to make things better for the sick and wounded men.

When the war ended Florence Nightingale went home. She was a heroine. Everyone wanted to welcome her and show how much they thought of her work, but she went quietly into the country to her parents' house. Soon she went to live in London. She spent the rest of her long life arranging for the training of nurses, improving army hospitals, sending medical teams to India, studying, writing, arguing and bullying politicians. So the next time you visit a hospital and watch smart nurses looking after people in the spotless wards think of the woman who made it possible by giving her life to the care of the suffering.

Martin Luther King

The man waited patiently, his rifle at the ready. He looked out of the open window of the bathroom at the hotel balcony, not seventy yards away. At last his moment came. A man stepped out on to the balcony and began to chat with three men in the courtyard below. He was a neatly-dressed black man. The rifle was raised and its owner squinted along its telescopic sights. He squeezed the trigger. The man on the balcony fell and was dead before his friends got him to hospital. Within minutes the news was being flashed around the world: 'Dr Martin Luther King is dead.'

Martin Luther King was born in the southern part of the United States of America. His father was a minister. Martin was a clever boy whose ambition was to be a doctor. Later he changed his mind and became a minister, much to the pleasure of his father. He began his life as a minister in a city named Montgomery.

Soon after he arrived there a black woman was arrested for sitting in a bus seat which was reserved for white people only. The driver had asked her to move to the back seats set aside for black passengers and she had refused. Now she was in prison for breaking one of the city's laws. Some of the leaders of the black citizens decided to do all they could for her. They held a meeting to which Dr King came. It was

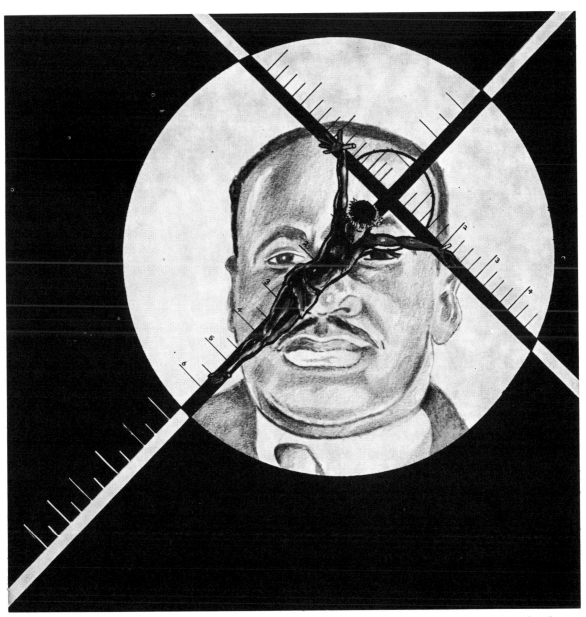

decided to persuade as many black people as possible to stop using the buses. As most of the bus users were black this would mean that the bus company would lose a great deal of money and would either have to go out of business or else give way to demands that passengers of either colour could sit where they liked in the city buses.

They quickly made Martin Luther King their leader. He told his people of the plan and they carried it out almost to a man. Many walked to work, even if it was a long way. Others who had cars gave lifts to those who had none. Taxi owners carried black passengers for the price of a bus ride. All the black people in Montgomery, spurred on by Dr King, were determined to win this battle with the rulers of their city. They walked for more than a year before the bus company gave in.

After this Dr King was known all over the United States. His people admired him and listened to his words. He told them that the struggle had just begun. They must fight for the right of black people to mix with whites in schools, shops, cafés and all public buildings. They must fight to obtain the votes and jobs that the white man was so unwilling to give them. But, said Dr King, they must not fight with weapons; that was wrong. They must fight by going where they were forbidden and then allowing themselves to be arrested. They must go to jail if necessary. If attacked they must not defend themselves. They must show that, they were willing to suffer and even die to win simple rights for their people. They were not trying to *beat* their enemies but to make them feel ashamed.

For the rest of his life Martin Luther King led his people in their struggle. He preached, wrote, spoke on television, led marches, sat in whites-only shops and travelled wherever he could help. Gradually he brought many people round to his way of thinking. Others, however, still looked on him as a troublemaker, out to turn the world upside-down and make black people masters of the whites. His followers were often brutally attacked, sometimes by the police. He himself was thrown in jail many times, hit by a rock and once stabbed. On one occasion a bomb exploded on the front porch of his house. Luckily no-one was injured.

Dr King's work began to produce results. The government passed laws outlawing the separation of blacks and whites in schools and public buildings. White city rulers came to realize that they could not fight forever the determined black people. Dr King turned his attention to the northern cities where many blacks lived in great poverty. He taught them how to press for better homes and better jobs.

Because of his work for his people Martin Luther King was widely loved and widely hated, and the day he stepped on to the balcony the hatred found its chance. The man died, but the work he did to free his people will never die.

Faithful Dog

Tom lived in what the Australians call the outback, the great open spaces in which the neighbouring farm may be fifty miles away. He had no playmates on the small sheep-farm which his parents ran so they bought him a fluffy puppy to keep him company. Tom was delighted. Every day he would take Scruff out to the nearby hills and they would roll and play, hunt rabbits and chase kangaroos until the sun dipped behind the hills.

The years passed. Tom was eighteen and Scruff was a fully-grown dog when war broke out in 1939. Tom decided that he should join the army and fight against the Germans. So one day he put on his knapsack and said good-bye to his parents. They stood outside the farm, close to tears, as the boy set off. Scruff, who had gone everywhere with Tom, trotted along at his heels. Tom stopped and said, 'Not this time, old fellow,' and shooed the dog back to the old couple. They watched until Tom disappeared over the brow of the hill and then went indoors sadly.

Next day they found Scruff lying on the road at noon, his eyes fixed on the road. He was waiting for his master's return. He stayed there for hours and finally came indoors, his tail drooping with disappointment. He did the same thing the next day and the next, and the pattern repeated itself from then on.

Soon they received a cheerful letter from Tom. He was in Europe, he told them, but they must not worry about him.

But of course they did. The newspapers were full of stories about fierce fighting in France. Tom's letters became rarer as he found himself in the battle area. Then one dreadful day a letter came from the Australian government telling them that Tom was 'missing, believed killed'.

The old couple were shattered. Tom was their only child, their whole family. Their lives seemed nothing without him. They didn't care about anything any more. Only Scruff seemed not to be affected. He continued to lie in the road at mid-day, staring at the hill where his master had gone away so long ago.

Nobody was surprised when Tom's father grew ill and died. 'He didn't want to live,' they said. And when, not long after, his mother passed away, they simply shook their heads. Two neighbours took Scruff to live at their farm twenty miles away. Next morning he was gone. They found him at noon next day at his post outside the boarded-up farm, gazing patiently up the road. They took him to their home. He ran away again. They fetched him back. He ran away. So they gave up.

Scruff then became a wild dog, living in the brush and eating what he could kill by hunting. His coat grew dirty and his body thin. But every day he took up his position in the road when the sun was hottest, and waited. Hours later he would rise and lope off sadly back into the brush. Now and then a stranger would come down the dirt road. Scruff would rise, ears pricked, and watch until his failing eyesight told him that it was not Tom. Then he would slink off once again.

A year passed. Scruff was slower now and there was plenty of grey around his mouth. He could not run so quickly and food was scarce. His bones could be clearly seen through his filthy coat.

One day he took up his post on the road, his muzzle resting on the ground, his tired old eyes fixed on the hill. A figure came over the crest. Scruff raised his head but did not move. The stranger approached. Something about the swing of his arms, the set of his shoulders, brought the dog to his feet, his eyes straining to see more clearly. Then he moved forward, at first slowly, then more quickly, and finally he broke into a run and flung himself into Tom's arms. The soldier stood there for a long time hugging the old dog, tears running down his cheeks and on to Scruff's filthy coat. Then they went inside the farm to start their lives again. The dog's loyalty and affection were finally rewarded.

William Booth

Not long after Queen Victoria came to the throne a boy named William Booth took a job as a pawnbroker's apprentice in the city of Nottingham. Pawnbrokers are shop-keepers who will take some valuable object like a watch or a coat and lend you money while they keep it. Later you can buy it back for a little more than the pawn-broker lent you. Naturally these shops are mostly used by very poor people and young William quickly saw what miserable lives many of them led. Work was scarce and wages pitifully small. Often, he knew, men were pawning their household treasures for the drink that would help them forget for one happy evening the hopelessness of their grey lives.

William was a religious boy who went regularly to the Methodist church. Indeed, he hoped one day to become a Methodist minister. He loved to attend open-air meetings to listen to great preachers of those days. When he was seventeen he decided to set up as a preacher himself. He delivered his first sermon in a private house standing behind a table.

Soon William became dissatisfied with his own church. He thought that his fellow-Christians were too self-satisfied, too concerned with saving their own souls and not eager enough to save others. He also believed that they did not do enough for the desperately poor people he saw around him every day. One Sunday he took some tramps into his church and the good people were disgusted. They forced him to take them to the back of the church where they would not be seen. William protested that these were the very people they should be trying to help.

By this time William Booth felt that he had a great task to perform. He left for London, where he joined up with other Christians and went about the great city preaching. He was a fine speaker and soon came to be known as a man who could lead others. He was asked to tour the whole country, which he at once agreed to do.

For many years William Booth went up and down Britain, persuading thousands to change their lives and become Christians. During this time he married and became the father of eight children. His wife became one of the first women preachers in the country.

When William was thirty-six years old he went back to London and took over an open-air mission held in a tent. The tent was wrecked by hooligans and he moved to a dance room. This proved unsatisfactory, so he moved to the back room of a pigeon-shop. He changed headquarters several times in the next few years until he found a suitable home in a disused pub.

These were great years for William Booth. He gathered around him a fine group of helpers and set up several soup kitchens. These were places where down-and-outs could get a free meal. A magazine was founded to spread William's ideas.

Fourteen preaching stations were set up at which 140 services a week took place. People of London's East End got used to the sight of these new missionaries at street corners; they wore red and black uniforms and played cheerful hymns on their brass instruments. Because William Booth spoke so often about salvation – that is, being saved from sin and hell – and because he said that his followers were soldiers fighting against wickedness they became known as the Salvation Army.

Thousands of people, moved by the way the Army cared for the poor, helped William. Rich men gave him money to aid his work. Branches of the Army were set up all over Britain and eventually all over the world. Naturally this created an immense amount of work for the man who started it all, but he tackled it all with the help of his tireless wife and children.

William Booth became 'General' Booth, for armies need generals. His helpers also became colonels, majors, and so on, on the model of real armies. But this army, as everyone came to realize, was different. Its enemies were sin and poverty. Nobody suffered from its attacks.

However, not everyone was pleased to see the Salvation Army grow. Some people were shocked by the brass bands and merry hymns. Others said that feeding the poor was simply bribing them. Many Army meetings were broken up by hooligans, and the followers of William Booth often finished their day's work bruised and bleeding. But this did not stop them. 'The Sally Army', as it came to be called, went from strength to strength. When its founder died at the great age of eighty-three it had spread all over the world, and was widely regarded as a force for good in a troubled world.

Now, a hundred years after William Booth started it, the Salvation Army runs thirty-one hospitals, twenty-one rescue homes for women, thirteen schools for difficult boys and girls, eighty-eight homes for unmarried mothers, one hundred and thirty-seven old people's homes, one hundred and thirty-nine slum posts, twenty-one homes for alcoholics and four hundred and four hostels for the homeless. So perhaps that's why they always look so cheerful at their street-corner meetings.

Albert Schweitzer

In the early years of this century Albert Schweitzer was world-famous. He was a fine musician, a successful writer and a preacher in demand all over Europe. In addition, he had an important teaching post at a great university. He seemed to be everyone's idea of a successful man, one who would live the rest of his life in comfort and with the growing respect of his fellow-men.

One day he read about how miserably many people in Africa lived. He learned with a feeling of shame that thousands died every year because there were no doctors or hospitals. He made up his mind at once. He would become a doctor and do something about it. He went to medical school. He worked hard for six years and passed his examinations. Now he was ready for Africa.

When his friends heard that he was really going they could hardly believe it. They told him he was foolish, that the climate would kill him and his wife and that he could do more good for Africans by preaching about their misery in Europe. They tried hard to make him change his mind. But it was no use. He sailed for Africa as soon as he could.

He was sent to a village in the hottest, unhealthiest part of what was then called 'the Dark Continent'. Disease was widespread. The only medical attention the people received was from native witchdoctors, most of whom knew nothing of modern ways of dealing with illness. Schweitzer decided that the first thing to do was build a hospital. He had no money, tools, workmen or materials, so he cleaned out a henhouse and placed an ordinary table near the door. On this he neatly arranged his medicine bottles. Then he sat down and waited for his first patients.

And they came. At first they were suspicious, but when they found that the new medicine worked they flocked to Schweitzer's little hospital. Soon he was working from morning till night, bandaging wounds, delivering babies and even performing operations. The people came to love and trust him.

He enlarged his building and many helpers came to share the work. Things were going well, but then war broke out in Europe. At first Schweitzer was not affected but later – being a German in a part of Africa ruled by France – he was taken away to France. While he was there he wrote a book.

When the war ended he went on an organ-playing tour to make money for his hospital. Then he went back to Africa and proceeded to knock down his old shacks and build a new, modern hospital. By this time more and more people had heard of Schweitzer's work, and doctors, nurses and other helpers arrived to give their services. Many others sent money, drugs, medicines and building materials.

By now Schweitzer was an old man. His friends kept asking him when he would go back home after his many years of hard work. Never, was the reply. He would stay

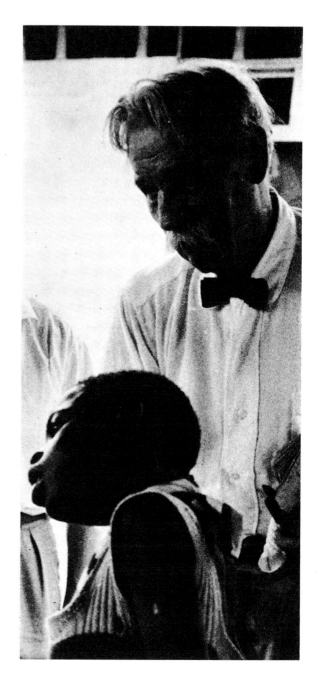

in Africa until he died. And so he remained there until his death in 1965, leaving his work to remind us how much he did for other people.

Emmeline Pankhurst

A woman's place is in the home, doing the housework and looking after the children. She should not be allowed to become, say, a lawyer or a business manager, for her mind is not made for those things.

Such were the opinions most men held when your great-grandmother was a little girl. Some women thought these ideas were a lot of nonsense. They said that women were just as bright and well-informed as men and should have the same rights. They should be allowed to vote, become members of Parliament and own their own property. In those days women had none of these rights. As time went on more and more people – men as well as women – began to get together and demand them.

Their leader was Emmeline Pankhurst. She was a married woman with a family. Her home was in Manchester but she moved to London to carry on her fight for women's rights. And what a fight it became! At first she tried all the usual ways of making members of Parliament in this country change the laws; she held meetings, wrote letters, approached important people and gave lectures. This brought very little success. Even many women were angry with Mrs Pankhurst for what they called her unladylike behaviour. Most men thought she was a foolish crank. One wag claimed that she had said to her followers,

'Ladies, put your faith in God. *She* will look after you.'

At last she decided that she and her friends – now widely known as suffragettes,

which means 'women seeking the vote' – were getting nowhere. Mrs Pankhurst ordered her followers to become public nuisances, to break the law if necessary and be sent to prison to bring the lawmakers to their senses.

The suffragettes needed no urging. They sprang into action. They hurled bricks at public speakers, smashed the windows of Number 10 Downing Street, slashed paintings in art galleries, chained themselves to the railings outside politicians' houses and generally broke the law in as many different ways as they could think of. When brought before the courts they even refused to pay the fines and were put in prison. Mrs Pankhurst went to prison many times for her actions.

Still the lawmakers refused to give women the vote, although more and more people were coming to believe that it was the right thing to do. It seemed as if neither side could get the other to give way in this bitter battle.

The First World War broke out. Hundreds of thousands of young men joined up and went to France to fight. Mrs Pankhurst told her followers to stop their work for the vote and do everything they could to help win the war. That was the most important thing, she said. All other aims could wait until after the war was won.

The suffragettes obeyed her. Many of them took jobs in the great factories which made guns and explosives. Many became nurses and ambulance drivers, working long hours in dirty and dangerous places within sound of the guns. Every place left empty when a soldier went off to war was filled by a woman eager to show that she could work as hard and as well as the man whose place she had taken.

Soon the whole country was so impressed by the behaviour of the women that it became only a matter of time before Parliament gave them the vote. It did so in the last year of the war, but only to women over thirty. This did not satisfy Mrs Pankhurst who declared that she would not stop until women had the same rights as men. She carried on speaking, writing and lecturing for what she believed.

Ten years later she won. Parliament passed a law giving the vote to all persons over twenty-one. On the day it passed Emmeline Pankhurst, now an old lady of nearly seventy-one, died.

Every woman who has lived in this country since then has had reason to be grateful to Emmeline Pankhurst. She helped to change people's ideas about women and she won important rights for them by the way she fought and suffered.

Thomas Edison

Six-year old Tom Edison wondered what would happen if he set fire to his father's barn. He was so curious about this that he could not stop himself from putting a light to it. The little boy found that his experiment had two results; first, the barn burned to the ground and second, his father put him across his knee and spanked him. It was a painful start to the career of a great inventor.

Thirty years later the young fire-raiser was the best-known scientist on earth. He was praised everywhere for hundreds of inventions which included the record-player and the electric light bulb. He was, they said, a wizard, a genius. This sort of talk annoyed Edison, who said, ' Genius is one per cent inspiration and ninety-nine per cent perspiration.' By this he meant that a new idea is far less important than the hard sweat needed to make it work. His invention of the electric light bulb seemed to back up what he said.

When Edison first declared that he was going to produce electric lighting he was told not to waste his time. It was impossible, said one scientist after another; the laws of nature would not allow it. Edison paid no attention but plunged into the problem with his usual energy. He read every book he could get his hands on which dealt with lighting and from them he took notes and sketches that filled two hundred notebooks. After long study he decided how he would create his new light. He would pass an electric current through a thin thread of metal. The metal, soon heated by the current, would begin to glow, giving the world a kind of light that was different from anything it had ever seen before.

Eagerly Edison took some metals and had them shaved down to fine strands. He placed them in position and passed an electric current through them. They were no good. Some of them gave out a little light but the current quickly burned them out. Edison took more metals and tried them. None worked. But he firmly believed that somewhere there must be a substance whose threads would shed light and yet be strong enough to stand being heated. He tried many thousands of materials from cardboard to human hairs, and at last he found what he was looking for. He discovered that thin strips of bamboo warmed by electricity in a glass bulb gave enough light and were tough enough to make electric lighting possible.

An even greater task now faced Edison. It was one thing to make an electric lamp that worked in the laboratory, but quite another to install lighting in the homes of New York, which Edison quickly agreed to do. For a start, there were no factories making the machinery he needed. He made it himself with the help of workers whom he instructed at all stages of the job. Then the streets of New York had to be dug up to lay the wires leading to the houses. Next he had to invent a meter to tell how much electricity each home used. These and a thousand other problems needed to be solved by the only man who understood them – Thomas Edison.

And solve them he did. After years of effort – years during which he managed only a few hours' sleep a night, and those often spent on the factory floor – his work was finished. A switch was turned, and the city glistened with electric light.

To the end of his life he continued by his hard work to turn out inventions that made men's lives easier or happier. You will use two of them tonight if you go home and switch on the light and the record-player.

Saladin

Nearly eight hundred years ago the Christian countries heard the terrible news that the Saracens had captured the Holy City of Jerusalem. In every village rumours ran wild. These Saracens, it was said, were the wicked followers of Muhammad, and did not believe that Jesus was the Son of God. Their cruel leader, a king named Saladin, had cut every Christian throat in the city and would never allow the faithful to pray at the holy places which Jesus had seen and touched. The great kings and princes were collecting a mighty army to free Jerusalem from the rule of these savages.

The Christian army was led by Richard the First of England, called Lionheart for his bravery. The English admired their warrior-king and their hearts swelled with pride when he sailed from Dover. Richard and his Crusaders – 'Crusader' means 'marked with a cross' – would soon throw the Saracens out of Jerusalem. They looked forward to his return. They longed for battle stories, for tales of Christian bravery and Saracen cowardice, and to hear how their honest Richard had beaten the treacherous Saladin.

Nearly three years later the English knights came home without Richard, who had been captured on his way back from the wars by an enemy. When they were pressed to tell of their adventures in the Holy Land they told stories which were very different from those their listeners expected. Most surprising was what they had to say about the Saracen leader, Saladin.

'Saladin', it seemed, was not his real name but a nickname which meant 'honour of the faith'. His people called him this because he had studied deeply and followed carefully the rules of his religion. Until the age of twenty-six he had been a quiet, bookish young man. Then, because he came from a family of soldiers, he was unwillingly drawn into a war in Egypt. He soon showed that he was a good soldier. The men under his command knew that he always thought deeply and prepared thoroughly before every battle. During the fighting he rode here and there encouraging his men without taking unnecessary risks, but if things were going badly he would plunge into the thick of the battle. Within a short time he was widely admired, and in just over ten years he became king of Egypt and Syria, two countries which covered a very wide area.

He ruled over a great swathe of land, broken only by a thin strip of territory which we now call Israel, but which was then called the Holy Land. Its chief city was Jerusalem. The Crusaders had captured it nearly a hundred years before.

Now Saladin longed to take back the Holy Land and its ancient city. He found a good excuse when a Christian knight twice attacked his people. The Saracen army swept through the Holy Land, crushed the Christian troops, and advanced on Jerusalem. The citizens shook with terror, fearing that they would be slaughtered as the Saracens had been when the first Crusaders had captured the city. They need not have worried. When Saladin forced his way into Jerusalem he allowed the Christians to buy their freedom. The ancient buildings were left untouched.

Four years later Richard arrived in the Holy Land in company with many European princes and the best of their knights. He captured the city of Acre and killed more than two thousand prisoners. Then he won a fine victory against Saladin's army. But by now the Christian princes were quarrelling among themselves. Many went back home, leaving Richard with a weakened army to fight on. After a year of war Richard knew that he had no chance of capturing Jerusalem. He made peace with Saladin. The two men agreed that the Christians were to keep some of the seaports near Jerusalem and were to be allowed to visit the city when they wanted. On his way home Richard was taken prisoner by a fellow-Crusader who demanded a huge sum for his release.

All this the returned knights told their friends. Saladin, they said, was a man who always kept his word and Richard was not. Saladin was gentle and merciful; Richard was given to bursts of uncontrollable anger in which he performed great cruelties. Saladin admired Richard's bravery and sent him fruit and snow as he lay ill under a sweltering sun. His army, too, fought rather more honourably than the Crusaders. The Christian princes disgraced themselves by their greedy squabbling and by scuttling home when the fighting got rough. The capture and ransoming of Richard, the bravest and best Crusader, by a comrade-in-arms sickened everyone who believed that the war was being fought for a noble purpose.

These stories surprised the people who had always thought that they were the goodies and their enemies were the baddies. They helped them to realize that the strangers who seemed so different from them were as good as, if not better than, themselves.

The Prince's Chiming Watch

(Adapted from *Historiettes*
by Gédéon Tallemant des Réaux)

Once upon a time – and this is a true story even though it begins with 'once upon a time' – the King of France had a brother about whom there were two very different opinions. Strangers found him cross. They said that he was puffed-up with his own importance, always aware that royal blood flowed in his veins. Angrily they told the story of how he had had a man ducked in the canal for not showing proper respect to him, or so he claimed.

His friends said there was another side to his nature – a better side. He was more than kind to people he liked, they said, and found it easy to forgive people who had done him wrong. Take the story of the prince's gold watch, for example. Then they would enjoy telling this odd tale.

One night the prince held one of his parties to which he invited all his friends. The great room was gay with the noise of lords and ladies gossiping, laughing, dancing or simply listening to the music. Here and there the smiling prince strolled, shaking a hand here, making a joke there and seeing that everyone was well supplied with food and drink.

Towards the end of the night the prince put his hand in his pocket to take out his watch. That was his polite signal that his guests should leave. To his surprise the watch was not there. A quick search of his other pockets revealed that it was not to be found. He distinctly remembered having seen it since the party had started. There was only one conclusion. The watch had been stolen by someone in the room.

The prince told his closest friends what had happened. They were shocked into silence. They all knew and admired the watch – a gold one made with great labour by the finest craftsmen. Meanwhile the other guests had seen the serious faces of the prince and his inner circle of friends. Soon the news had spread all over the room and the people grew silent, waiting to see what the prince would do.

At last one man spoke aloud. 'Sire,' he said, 'I think I speak for all your true friends when I say that we are greatly distressed at the theft of your watch. May I suggest that the door be locked so that none of us may leave. Then I am sure that none but the thief will mind being searched. In that way we are certain to recover your splendid timepiece.'

The prince smiled. 'I am grateful for the suggestion,' he said. 'I could indeed regain my watch in that way, but it would mean losing a friend. By the way, it is a chiming watch which is due to strike the hour very soon. As the chimes will certainly give the thief away I should be pleased if you would all go home now to protect the person who took it.'

Open-mouthed, the guests filed silently out of the room, amazed that anyone should be so anxious to shield someone who had stolen from him. So ever after that when anyone criticized the prince one of his admirers would tell the true story of the chiming watch.

Helen Keller

When Helen Keller was a toddler of eighteen months she caught a fever which carried her to the brink of death. For days her parents watched over the cot while their little girl tossed and sweated. Then the fever left her and the child slept peacefully. Her parents were overjoyed, but not for long. You see, they soon found out that Helen was blind and deaf.

For the next six years the Keller family did everything they could for the child. They washed her, fed her, taught her to walk and did the million other things that her afflictions prevented her from doing for herself. Soon after she lost her hearing she became dumb too, for children need to hear people speaking in order to be able to talk.

You can imagine what it must have been like for that little girl if you close your eyes, put cotton-wool in your ears and pretend that you cannot talk. But imagine what it would be like to remain like that for an entire lifetime. Imagine what it would be like not to be able to get in touch with a single person, ever. That is what seemed to face Helen Keller.

Then Annie Sullivan came into her life. Annie was a teacher of the blind, twenty-one years old, just out of training. She came to look after Helen at the suggestion of one of the many doctors Mr and Mrs Keller consulted.

Annie found out straight away that

Helen was a dreadful child. Her parents had been too sorry for her to make her behave even fairly well. She bit, kicked, disobeyed, ran away, ate like a pig from her own and others' plates and in short was the wildest, most unmanageable child that Annie had ever seen.

Anne decided that the first thing she had to do was tame the child. She put her foot down from the start. She insisted that Helen do as she was told. When she ran away from the table Annie dragged her back. When she smacked Annie's face Annie smacked hers. Within a day or two Helen knew that Annie was the boss and that she would have to do what her teacher ordered. Mind you, Annie was not entirely rough with the child. She showed by stroking and caressing her that she really liked her and that she was only acting in this way for her own good.

After a month Annie began to teach Helen the deaf and dumb alphabet. This is done by taking the dumb person's hand and making finger signs in the palms. It is hard to teach it to people who have at one time been able to hear and speak. It is almost impossible for someone to learn it who has been blind and deaf almost since birth. So Annie knew when she began that a great task stretched ahead of her.

To her astonishment Helen picked up the finger alphabet with wonderful speed. Once she got the idea that this was a way she could speak to people she did not rest until she had mastered it. Then, again at lightning speed, she learned Braille, a system of raised dots which helps blind people to read. Here was a very intelligent child, thought Annie, and she pressed on with the girl's education. Later, at a special school, Helen learned to talk.

The world had changed for Helen Keller. True, it was still dark and silent, but now she could open her mouth and speak to people and listen, through the finger alphabet, to their replies. She could sit down with one of her Braille books and, by running her fingers along the page, find out more about the unseen, unheard world from which she had seemed so cruelly cut off. Her wildness disappeared. She turned from a little savage into a gentle, educated person within a few years. Naturally if Annie had not come it all would never have happened.

At twelve Helen wrote her first story. At twenty she went to college. Annie went with her and sat beside her at lectures, translating what the lecturer said into finger-language for her pupil. At twenty-two Helen wrote her life story. Soon it was translated into fifty languages and Helen became world famous.

She spent the rest of her life in activities which would have worn out a normal woman. With Annie she went on lecture tours, made films, wrote books and articles, travelled and appeared on the stage. In her later years she spent most of her time helping the blind. Together she and Annie Sullivan, by determination and effort, achieved things that would have seemed impossible to Helen's parents when she was a child.

Isaac Newton

The British bury many of their famous men in Westminster Abbey. There are kings, generals, admirals and others who in their life time enjoyed great power. But perhaps the greatest man whose body rests in this sacred place was Isaac Newton.

He was born in a village in Lincolnshire on Christmas Day, more than three hundred years ago. When he went to school his teachers did not think he was any cleverer than many other children. One of them said he was a dreamy boy, but very good with his hands. Young Isaac was to prove his teachers wrong and to show that you cannot always tell from a child's performance at school how much good work he can do when he grows up.

Isaac left school when he was a teenager and helped on his mother's farm. But he did not really enjoy it and at the age of nineteen he went up to Cambridge University. There he at once found the things that were to take up all his time and interest for the rest of his life – mathematics and science. He worked so hard that he soon learned all that his teachers had to offer him.

When plague – a widespread disease – struck the country all the students were sent home. He spent the summer studying, and made many wonderfully exciting discoveries about light, gravity, colours and

numbers. He wrote about these new ideas in a big book which he published some years later.

Isaac went back to the university and became a teacher there. He carried on his studies into many branches of science. He made the first reflecting telescope to search the secrets of the stars.

Isaac Newton set up house in Cambridge. He never married and his house was run by a housekeeper. The poor woman must have often lost patience with the great scientist. She used to bring his meals into his workroom and leave them on the bench while Isaac worked out some hard problem. When she returned hours later she often found that he had not touched a thing and the meal sat cold on the plate. He had been too wrapped up in his work to think of food.

This way of life went on for many years. Isaac, when he put his mind to a problem, slaved away at it until he found the answer. And how many answers he found! Some say that no scientist has ever given us as much new knowledge as Isaac Newton did. It is certain that he changed the whole picture of the world we live in. He taught all men that nothing in Nature cannot be understood if we are willing to use time, brains and effort to do so.

Newton became *Sir* Isaac Newton and entered Parliament. He was made Master of the Royal Mint, a very important post in those days. All over the world people looked up to him as the wisest of men. Yet he never changed his ways, remaining the same down-to-earth character he had always been. When men praised his knowledge he said he had only picked up a few pebbles from the shore of learning.

As he grew older Newton came to think that all his new discoveries about light, mathematics and the stars were unimportant compared with the study of the Bible. He spent more and more of his time poring over the sacred books of the Christians, trying to seek out the inner meanings of the scriptures as he had winkled out the secrets of Nature.

When he died at the age of eighty-four he was laid to rest with many of the country's finest sons and daughters in Westminster Abbey.

Margaret Haughery

If you ever go to New Orleans in the United States, you are sure to find out about Margaret Haughery. You may see her statue, which stands in a quiet square. It shows her as a short, ordinary-looking little woman wearing a plain dress, sensible shoes and a shawl. Her arms are around a child, who leans against her. If you ask her story you will hear a remarkable tale.

Margaret was a happy young woman with a husband and baby when disaster struck. First her husband and then her child died, leaving her alone in the world. She had to go out and earn her living. Luckily she was strong and willing, and she soon got a job ironing clothes in a laundry.

Opposite the window where Margaret sat ironing all day there was an orphanage – a home for children who have lost their parents. Margaret felt sorry for the boys and girls she saw working and playing there and decided to do something to help them. First she went to the nuns who ran the orphanage and arranged to give part of her weekly wages to help them. Then she set to work to save as much of the rest of her money as she could, for she had had a splendid idea.

Soon she had saved enough money and she bought two cows and a little cart. Then she started delivering milk every morning. At the big hotels and rich houses she asked

Margaret earned the large sums of money needed to keep her orphanage going. She sold a great deal of bread but she always kept some to give away free to those who could not afford to buy it.

By this time Margaret had become famous all over the city for her kindness to the poor. Some said that she must have no money of her own, so much did she give away. This was not true, for Margaret handled her business so well that she soon built a large modern factory to produce her loaves. This again meant that she could earn more money to help the orphan children she loved so much.

When Margaret died she left all her money – and she had saved quite a lot – to the different children's homes of the city. She signed her will with a cross instead of her name, because she had never learned to read and write.

for left-over food for the orphan children. Every morning she set off with her churns of milk and returned with a cartful of food which they were delighted to eat. Margaret gave most of the money she made from her milk round to the orphanage, but she was such a good businesswoman that in no time she was able to buy more cows and enlarge her round.

With the larger profits that she now made Margaret built a new orphanage for babies. Then she had a fresh idea. She bought a bakery and changed her trade. From then on she delivered bread instead of milk. Again her business did well and

Henri Dunant

A young man, his eyes glittering with excitement, sped towards the battlefield in a coach drawn by two horses. He hoped to get there before it began. In his mind's eye he pictured the scene. Slim, scarlet-coated soldiers sat stiffly on prancing horses, sabres held upright and gleaming in the sun. Cannons were already beginning to boom, dotting the sky with smoky puffs. Trumpet blasts and the slow, rhythmic rattle of drums drew the great lines of men steadily nearer each other. Sharp voices barked orders on the green slopes and the uniformed figures obeyed immediately.

Henri Dunant thought that the scene must be almost beautiful. He remembered the mock battles of his childhood, played on the carpet with lead soldiers. No lead soldiers, he thought, can surely compare with the gaily-uniformed heroes of flesh and blood.

He was too late to see the battle. When he got there he found a terrible sight. He saw men screaming in their death agonies, headless corpses, badly injured soldiers lying unattended while their wounds crawled with maggots, and pitifully few doctors trying to cope with the thousands of wounded. That was the worst shock of all for Henri Dunant. The dead were beyond help, but a wounded man would be lucky if he was picked up by a stretcher party from among the masses of injured men. Even then the makeshift hospital to which he was taken might be overrun by the enemy and all the patients slaughtered.

Henri Dunant set to work to help the wounded and dying. He stayed there for three days and nights, during which he came to understand and detest war. It was not the glorious test of bravery that armchair warriors imagined. It was madness and savagery.

When he left Solferino, where the battle had taken place, Dunant was a different man. He knew that men would always go to war. But he was determined to change its rules, or rather to give it some rules for the first time, for everyone believed at that time that there was no way of forcing rules on a country at war. He wrote a book about the battle of Solferino to show people exactly what war was like. He travelled all over Europe seeking out kings and generals and anyone who would listen to him. We must, he insisted, set up a medical service in every country which will, in the event of war, save the thousands of wounded men who die on battlefields through lack of care. We must lay down that doctors and hospitals must not be attacked. We must give even savage war some civilized laws.

The response to his book and his speeches was enormous. Most sensible men agreed at once that Dunant was right — that we just cannot fight without rules. He had many helpers. Five years after the battle of Solferino Dunant called a great meeting at Geneva, his home city. This became known as the Geneva Convention, and was one of the most important meetings of the great powers there has ever been. Strict rules were laid down for the conduct of war, and for the most part those rules have been kept ever since.

In many countries a medical service for use during war was set up. Since it had been agreed that its doctors, attendants and hospitals could not be attacked it became necessary to give it a symbol or flag to mark it clearly. A red cross on a white background was chosen and the service quickly became known as the Red Cross. There is now a Red Cross organization in nearly every country in the world. It is impossible to guess how many lives it has saved since it began more than a hundred years ago. In peacetime, too, it gives help during earthquakes, floods and other disasters.

The setting up of the Red Cross was a triumph for Henri Dunant but the rest of his life was sad. He neglected his business in trying to help other people, went bankrupt and vanished from public life. He was rediscovered as an old, bitter man, living alone and in poverty. He was awarded the Nobel peace prize, possibly the highest compliment any man can receive, but that did little to remove his sadness. But when he died, shortly before the First World War, people had come to realize that the Red Cross, born on the battlefield of Solferino, was one of the noblest ideas that had ever come to a human being.

The Actor and the Blind Man

Many years ago, when your grandfather was a little boy, every well-brought-up boy was expected to salute his grown-up neighbours – not a stiff, soldier's salute but a little touch of the forehead when passing them in the street. The habit was widespread not only in Britain but in France, where this story took place.

One day a well-known actor and his young son were walking along the street. On the other side the father saw a man standing holding out a tin mug. He wore dark glasses and around his neck hung a placard which read 'I am blind'. This was a common sight in those days, but every time the actor saw one of these blind beggars he was moved to pity.

He stopped, took a silver coin from his waistcoat pocket and said to his son, 'Go over and give this to the beggar.' The boy ran swiftly across the road and dropped the coin in the tin mug.

'God bless you,' said the beggar.

When the boy returned to his father he was surprised to see that he was looking at him rather crossly. 'What's the matter?' he asked.

'You didn't salute that beggar,' said his father.

The boy laughed. 'But he's blind,' he said. 'He couldn't see whether I saluted or not.'

'He may be a swindler,' said the actor. 'He may only be pretending to be blind.'

'Do you mean to tell me,' said his son, 'that you want me to salute even swindlers?'

'Yes,' said his father, 'Remember always that even if other people behave badly it does not give you the right to do so too. Make up your mind what is the right thing to do and do it, whatever anybody else may do.'

The boy never forgot his father's words.

Mother Teresa

Agnes was born in Yugoslavia shortly before the First World War. She grew up in a happy home with her brother and sister. As a little girl she used to listen in church to stories of the work done by priests and nuns in India. She made up her mind that one day she too would become a nun and help the miserable millions of that country. At the age of eighteen she set off for Ireland, where she received her early training. In the next year she went to Calcutta, India's biggest city, to begin the course of study and prayer that would make her a nun.

The next twenty years were happy ones for Sister Teresa, as she was now called. She became a teacher in a school for teenage girls. She loved the building with its grounds full of flowers. She enjoyed teaching very much. But as time went on she became more and more saddened by what she saw in the crowded streets of Calcutta. Naked, homeless and starving children wandered the pavements. Men and women crippled by leprosy – a disease that wastes the body – lay unattended in the gutters. At night it was impossible to walk more than a few paces without stumbling over one of the thousands who slept on the streets because they had no bed.

Mother Teresa – as she now was – felt that she had to do something about it. She gave up her post as head teacher and took a three months' course in nursing. Next she opened a school in a backyard in the slums. Five pupils turned up on the first day.

They had never been to school before. The number of pupils quickly grew. Help began to pour in as more people came to know what Mother Teresa was trying to do. Some of her former high school pupils joined her to teach the growing numbers. Well-wishers gave money, books, medicines – anything they could spare – to help the work.

Soon so many young nuns had joined Mother Teresa that she formed a separate order known as the Missionaries of Charity. She opened a home for the dying in a disused church. At once she was flooded with patients of all ages, some sick, many dying. Most had no home and no hope of getting into hospital. Many were lepers whose arms and legs ended hideously in stumps and whose families had put them out of their homes. Babies, left in dustbins by mothers who could not feed them, found their way into the home. Half of these sufferers died, but they died in comfortable beds knowing that everything had been done to save them by people who cared. Others were cured and started a new life with fresh hope.

Within a few years the sisters were looking after thousands. Many young men – doctors, teachers and other workers – flocked to help and became known as the Missionary Brothers of Charity. Other Indian cities, aroused by what Mother Teresa had done in Calcutta, opened their own homes, run by the sisters. The movement spread quickly to other countries. Centres sprang into being all over the world.

The first thing that strikes a visitor to Mother Teresa's homes is the happiness of the nuns. The second is their tenderness towards those in their care. When Mother Teresa was asked to explain this her reply was that the nuns are full of joy because they believe they are doing the work God wants them to do. As for their deep concern for every one of their patients, it springs from the belief that each person is a child of God and resembles Him, and so deserves care and love.

Booker T. Washington

Booker T. Washington was born more than a hundred years ago in a tumbledown shack in the United States of America. His skin was the colour of coffee, for he was the son of a Negro slave mother and a white man whom he never knew. His mother, a cook, worked on a cotton plantation. Her job was to prepare the food for the slaves who worked in the fields.

When Booker was big enough he too was given work to do. He became a waterboy. This meant carrying cans of water to refresh the slaves who sweated in the sun. Sometimes he was called up to the big house. There he pulled the rope that controlled the fans to cool the house. Every morning he carried the books of the daughters of the house to the school. Sometimes he would linger for a while watching the white children learning to read and write. He ached for book-learning, but there were no schools for Negroes. Indeed, many whites in those parts believed that black people were too stupid to learn.

When Booker was nine the slaves were freed and his mother took him to live with his stepfather. The boy was put to work in a salt-mine, packing the stuff in barrels. The hours were long and the job hard. Booker's wages were pitifully small and were snapped up by his stepfather. He was badly fed and had only one article of clothing – a shirt which he wore summer and winter.

In spite of the difficulties, Booker was determined to learn, not only because he hungered for knowledge, but because he knew that a good education could lead him away from the life of drudgery that stretched ahead of him. He begged his mother to get him a book – any book. She got him a spelling book. He had to teach himself the letters and words, for not a single Negro in the salt-mine could read.

Then Booker heard great news. A teacher had set up school in the village. Now, thought the boy, I'll really begin to learn. But his stepfather would not let him go because he did not want to lose his wages. He did let him go to night lessons, however, and young Booker picked up reading and writing at great speed. Later his stepfather allowed him to go to day school but insisted that he worked from four until nine o'clock in the morning, so that his money would still be coming in. Try to imagine yourself doing five hours of backbreaking work before coming to school and you'll get some idea of Booker's determination.

At sixteen the boy walked to another town to go to a higher school. He had to pay for his lessons there and to do so he persuaded the head to give him the job of school caretaker. So every evening Booker swept out the classrooms in which he had sat during the day. When the school closed for the summer holidays he worked in a restaurant. His teachers were very impressed by his intelligence and the energy with which he worked. They were

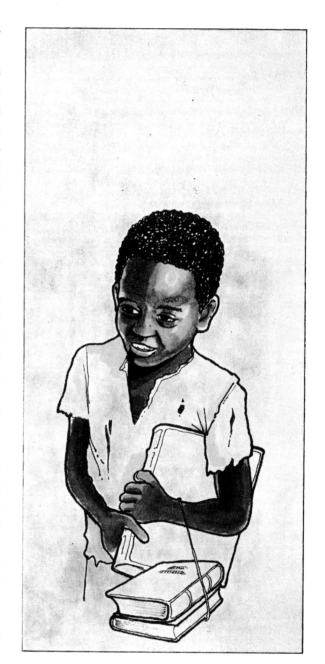

not at all surprised when he sailed through all his examinations and became a teacher in the village school where his education had begun.

For two years he taught black boys

who reminded him of the boy he had been ten years before. Then he left and spent eight months studying at a school in Washington. Next he took up a teaching post at his secondary school. People said he was a success. The black son of a slave had become Dr Washington, a well-qualified, respected person. Not many of his race, they said, had done as well.

Yet Booker himself was not satisfied. He longed to do more for his own people, whose lives were usually no better than slavery from birth to death. Education, thought the young teacher, was the answer. He must see to it that Negro boys had the chance to learn as he himself had had. Only by gaining and using knowledge could his people lift themselves out of their miserable state.

Soon afterwards he received an offer to open a Negro school at a place called Tuskegee. He jumped at it. This was just what he had been dreaming of. But when he got there he found that his school consisted of a leaky wooden church building and a rickety cabin. There were no desks or books. Worst of all, there were no students. Booker Washington rolled up his sleeves and put the place in order. Soon he opened with thirty pupils. Later that year he borrowed enough money to buy a large tract of wild land. He cleared the land with the help of his students and built a three-storey schoolhouse.

That was the beginning. Booker T. Washington spent the rest of his life working to make Tuskegee Institute a school where any clever Negro boy would receive a first-class education. As the buildings grew in number his name became widely known and highly regarded. He became the voice of the American Negro. Through speeches and books he spoke up for his people. Other schools, modelled on his, sprang up throughout the country and at last black children began to receive something like a good education.

For nearly thirty-five years Dr Washington worked at Tuskegee. When he died the institute consisted of more than a hundred buildings, two hundred teachers and 1,500 students, and Booker T. Washington had given learning and a new dignity to his race.

Mahatma Gandhi

Have you ever seen old maps of the world on which many of the countries are coloured red? Do you know what that means? It means that they were ruled by the British. One of the largest countries was India, a land with hundreds of millions of people, many of whom lived poor and miserable lives. Not only did the Indians hate the British who governed them, but most of them despised each other. The country was divided into many religious groups, each of which believed it was wrong to have anything to do with someone from another group.

The Indians longed to be free of British rule and to run their country in their own way. But they were helpless because of the power of the British and their own quarrelling. What they needed was a leader, a man who would be respected and obeyed, a man who would stand outside all the religions and classes.

One day a tiny thin man wearing Indian clothes got off a ship at Bombay. He was by this time quite famous, for he had spent more than twenty years in South Africa helping Indian people who had gone to live there. His name was Gandhi.

Gandhi believed that the most important thing for India was to get rid of the British, but he believed that this could never be brought about until the Indians

stopped fighting among themselves. He told his fellow-countrymen this as forcibly and as often as he could. This habit, he said, of looking down on people of different religion and different kind of family must stop. Their wise men had told them for

44

thousands of years to be kind to everyone. Now was the time to put it into practice. He himself would from now on treat all his race in exactly the same way.

'When we look on ourselves as one people,' said Gandhi, 'we can turn our attention to fighting the British. But we must not fight with guns. We must fight with our minds. We must be non-violent. We must refuse to obey British law. When the soldiers come to arrest us we must let them. We must go to prison for what we believe. We must make it impossible for the British to stay in India.'

Many Indians were taken with Gandhi's ideas and joined him. He was regarded as the great hope of his country. A poet called him 'Mahatma', that is, 'great soul', and it was by this name that he was known for the rest of his life. Indians felt that here was the leader they had always needed.

Gandhi threw all his energies into the struggle to free his country. He taught his followers what came to be called 'civil disobedience'. This meant doing everything possible to make the country hard to run. Gandhi's disciples, who by now numbered millions, would not fill in any of the forms a modern state asks its people to sign. They would not pay taxes which every government needs to provide roads, schools, hospitals and other public services. They held huge meetings at which Gandhi and other leaders spoke out against the severe laws.

As the years went by more and more Indians joined the Mahatma and demanded to be given back their own country.

At last the British realized that it was useless to stay where they were so clearly not wanted. In 1947 they left India to the Indians.

Gandhi should have been overjoyed but he was not. The British had had to divide this very large country into two countries, India and Pakistan, to meet the wishes of the two largest religions, Hindus and Muslims. Gandhi hated this division of his country and spoke, wrote and fasted against it, although he was now seventy-eight and thin, wizened and weak. But as he went to pray one day a man shot him three times and he died almost at once.

The world was saddened by Gandhi's death, for it had not seen anyone like him before. He had shown how to fight without injuring the enemy and how to persuade them by suffering.

The Sheep Stealer

There is a true story about two brothers who lived in a little English village long ago. Early in their childhood they began to steal. At first they took nothing very much – little odds and ends around their home – but as they grew older they got away with larger, more valuable objects. At last they came to believe that they were too clever to be caught. One day they stole a sheep from a neighbouring farm. They were arrested almost at once and brought before the judge. He found them guilty and ordered them to be branded. A red-hot iron, pressed to their foreheads, left the imprint of the letters ST there for the rest of their lives. 'ST' stood for 'sheep thief'.

Now this punishment, which seems so savage to us, was not looked on as especially cruel in those far-off days. 'After all,' people said, 'a sheep may be a man's entire wealth, the difference between plenty and poverty. And the pain from the burns wears off in a few days. Besides, other people must be warned that these men are thieves.'

When the two brothers had recovered from their wounds they talked about what they should do.

'I'm going away to a foreign country,' said one. 'I couldn't go back to the village and live there for the rest of my life with these letters stamped on my face. Imagine trying to live in a place where everyone can tell at a glance that you're a thief. No thanks, I'm off.'

'I don't see it that way,' said the other. 'I'm really sorry and ashamed for what I've done. I'm going back to see if I can live a better life. I feel that in time the villagers will forgive me and let me make up for the wrong I've done.'

His brother smiled grimly, shook hands, and set off for a foreign land. He found he could not settle there and moved on to another country. The people there were equally hard to live with. Their language and habits were very different from his own. His branded forehead made them mistrust him, although they did not understand what the letters meant. He travelled again to a distant land and set up another new home. But it was no good. He spent the rest of his life wandering from one land to another and finally died in a country far away. No one ever visited his grave.

Meanwhile his brother had gone back to the village. At first not a soul would speak to him and mothers passing in the street would draw their children closer. Everyone watched him suspiciously, waiting for his next theft. But he was really finished with stealing and all his other acts of wildness. He settled down to work hard not only for himself but for the villagers he had so often swindled. Soon it became known that he was helping his neighbours in every way that he could – with his labour, money, or advice. In no time the villagers knew they had a new man among them.

Many years later a stranger visited the

46

village. Noticing a grey-haired old man hobbling along with the letters ST on his forehead he asked a passing young man, 'Can you tell me, son, what those letters mean?' The young man said, 'I don't know. They were put there long ago, but no one remembers why. I expect it means something nice, for he's the wisest, kindest man here, a regular saint. Why, that's it!' cried the young man, smiling at his own cleverness, 'ST is short for "saint".'

Dr Barnardo

Round about the time your grandfather's grandfather was born Thomas John Barnardo was born in Dublin, the biggest city in Ireland. His father was a well-off dealer in furs. At the age of fourteen Thomas went to work in the office of a wine merchant. Soon he gave up this job because, he said, selling drink led to the widespread drunkenness he saw around him. This was the first sign of a change in his nature. He became much more serious and, his friends agreed, a true Christian.

At the age of twenty-one Thomas decided to become a missionary in China. He also made up his mind that he would become a doctor, so that he could look after the bodies as well as the souls of the Chinese.

He moved to London to study medicine. In his spare time he became an open-air preacher in the East End, London's poor district. He was appalled by what he found there. Hundreds of thousands of people led miserable lives in crumbling houses. Worse, the gas-lit alleys teemed with men and women who had no home, no job and no hope. Worst of all, thousands of children roamed the streets. They were the ones whose parents had died or deserted them. Many of them slept in the gutters and earned a living by begging or stealing.

Barnardo decided to forget about going to China. Here, on his own doorstep, there was enough work to last a man two life-

times. He gave up his medical studies and opened a home for boys who had lost their parents.

This was not as easy as it may sound. For a start, there were a lot of people who told him that it was just not possible – that London street urchins would wreck any home in a week. He was wasting his time and money. Then there was the task of raising money to buy the house and pay those who would run it. Everyone is in favour of raising money for good causes but not everyone is willing to put his hand in his pocket to help.

However, the first Dr Barnardo's Home opened, and from the beginning it was a great success. The East End street boys, far from wrecking their home, showed that they really appreciated it. Dr Barnardo saw to it that they were taught to read and write. He also arranged that each boy had the chance to learn a trade. Bible lessons were an important part of life in the home, for the doctor believed that only by knowing right from wrong, good from evil, could his boys lead a better life.

A few years later Dr Barnardo opened a home for girls, for it was clear to him that there were as many homeless girls as boys. By now his work was beginning to attract wide attention. Many people came forward to help. Others sent money. His name became well known and he felt encouraged to spread his work to other homes.

Dr Barnardo's Homes sprang up in many cities in Britain and other countries. There was now no scarcity of people willing to act as teachers, cooks, housemaids and handymen, but Dr Barnardo continued to work energetically himself. He continued for thirty-five years, during which time he brought up a family of seven children of his own.

When Dr Barnardo died at the age of sixty there were ninety of his homes. It was reckoned that he had rescued and trained more than 59,000 children – which is about the number of people at a big FA cup tie. He had helped for a time more than a quarter of a million children.

Since the doctor's death at the beginning of this century his homes have spread all over the world, and there is now no way of knowing how many children have been helped. Barnardo was not the first man to feel sorry for poor children but he was one of the first to set to and do something about it, by giving his time and energy, not just his sympathy.

Sir Philip Sidney

Some people's lives will always be remembered for one incident in them. Take Columbus, or Robert Bruce, or Yuri Gagarin. Sir Philip Sidney is always remembered for the way he died.

He was born into a noble family more than four hundred years ago. He went to Shrewsbury School as a boarder and at the age of eleven he could write letters to his father in French and Latin. From his childhood everyone spoke of his kindness and intelligence. He went to Oxford University, but he left at the age of seventeen when the plague struck and never went back.

During the next fifteen years he spent much time abroad representing Queen Elizabeth. He studied history, astronomy, music and many other branches of learning. He wrote poems and books. By the time of his death he was looked on as a perfect English gentleman.

At that time the Dutch were fighting the Spanish and a large number of Englishmen went to help the Dutch. Among them was Sidney. Before one battle Sidney was putting on his armour. Up rode a friend, Sir William Pelham, who had forgotten to put on his leg armour. Sidney laughed and threw off his own, saying that he would have no advantage over Sir William.

Sidney fought bravely in the battle. One horse was shot from under him and he fought on with another one. He received a shot from a musket-ball in the leg, a wound which his armour would have prevented. Lying on the battlefield, drenched with sweat and in great pain from his wound, Sidney asked for a cup of water to cool his burning mouth. Someone found him one, but just as he raised it to his lips a stretcher passed carrying a dying man. He looked longingly at Sidney's cup of water. Sidney said, 'Your necessity is greater than mine,' and gave him the cup.

His own wound grew quickly worse and shortly after the battle he died. If only for this one generous action people will never forget Sir Philip Sidney.

Anne Frank

On Anne Frank's thirteenth birthday she received a diary among her presents. She decided to name the book Kitty and tell it, or her, all the things she would not tell even her best friend. Anne was a pretty, bright, talkative girl. She loved her parents and greatly admired her clever sixteen-year old sister, Margot. The family lived in a city in Holland, which at that time was ruled by the Germans. They had taken it over not long before at the beginning of the Second World War.

Some time after Anne began to write her diary her sister was called up by the Germans. Now the Franks, being Jews, knew what this meant. It meant that Margot might be sent to one of the prison camps in Germany where Jews were starved or gassed to death. Mr Frank acted at once. He gathered as many of the family's belongings as he could and took his wife and daughters to live in a few secret rooms at the back of the office building where he worked. The stairs leading to these rooms were hidden by a bookcase.

The Franks were soon joined by another Jewish family consisting of the husband and wife and their teenage son, Peter. Later a dentist shared their hiding-place. These eight people lived in fear for more than two years. Kind friends brought them food and books. They listened anxiously for news of the war and were heartened when the enemies of Germany grew stronger and began to win many battles. There were bound to be quarrels among prisoners walled up for so long together, but none of them was really serious.

This imprisonment must have been hardest on Anne, who was the youngest. But there is no bitterness in her diary, not even against the people who kept her from freedom. Sometimes she grumbles about her fellow-prisoners, but always in a good-natured way, and she often admits that she herself can be hard to live with. Her diary tells the whole story of life behind the bookcase. We read of the narrow escapes from capture, the bickerings, the joys, the boredom and the long hours of reading. We find Anne, who at first thinks Peter dull, gradually falling in love with him and he with her.

Then the blow fell. The German security police found their hiding-place. They were all captured and sent to prison camps in Germany. Only one returned after the war – Anne's father.

Anne died of a fever only two months before the end of the war. She left her diaries, which the Germans had failed to find when they came to arrest the family. These little books show us how a brave girl faced long imprisonment and death with a light heart and a clear head.

Louis Braille

Monsieur Braille kept a saddler's shop in his white house at the corner of the village street. On the worn bench in the work-room lay lengths of leather and several tools which included a razor-sharp knife. One day Louis, the saddler's three-year old son, toddled into the shop when his parents' backs were turned, picked up the knife and a piece of leather, and began to cut as he had seen his father do. A moment later a wild scream brought his parents rushing in to find the boy bleeding from a wound in the eye. The village doctor did his best but could not save the sight of the eye, which quickly became diseased. Soon the other eye was affected and Louis Braille went blind.

At the age of ten the country boy won a scholarship to a school for blind children in Paris. His parents were pleased for this meant that their son would get a good education at the best place of its kind in the country. They packed his cases and sent him off on the coach.

Louis soon showed how clever he was. He worked hard at his lessons and won prize after prize. His teachers thought very highly of him. At the age of twelve he turned his mind to the problem of teaching blind children to read and write. He himself had learned to read by running his fingers over thin cardboard pages on which raised letters had been stamped. This sys-tem was slow and costly, and Louis was glad when a man named Charles Barbier invented a new one.

Barbier's idea was to punch raised dots on thick paper to represent letters which a blind person could 'read' with his fingertips. Later he changed the plan so that the dots made sounds, not letters. Louis Braille thought both ideas an improvement on what had gone before but that they were still not good enough. What blind people needed, he said, was a method that was simple and cheap. He set to work to make one. Night after night he worked – for he was still a schoolboy during the day. At last, after three years, he produced his alphabet for the blind. It was so much better than anything that had been used before that the experts were most impressed. It was tried in several schools and voted a great success. Slowly it spread through France. Louis's invention became known as Braille, and it has been known by that name ever since. It has come to be used in every country in the world.

Louis Braille spent the rest of his life as a teacher and organist, for he was a keen musician. In spite of his blindness and his bad health he was a kind and happy man. He died at the age of forty-three and was buried in the village graveyard at Coupvray, his birthplace. A hundred years after his death his body was taken to the Pantheon, a great building in Paris where the French bury those they respect greatly.

But for Louis Braille countless thousands who can now explore the world with their fingertips would have lived their lives in darkness and despair.

The French Valley

Many years ago a young man and his grandfather stood outside their farmhouse on the steep side of a French valley.

'Isn't it a shame,' said the young man, 'that we and our neighbours have to scratch a living from tiny farms on the rocky sides of this valley while there's all that flat land down below? I know it's nothing but marshland and always has been, and that it's far too soggy to farm, but I know how to change it into rich fields and I'm going to do it.'

His grandfather smiled. 'I know what you're going to say, Pierre,' he said. 'You're going to tell me that what we need are trees – thousands of them – planted on the slopes of the valley. The trees will gather soil around their roots and soak up the rainwater that flows down and turns the flat land into a bog. Well, it's been tried before and it's failed. You see, the streams are so strong that they carry away young trees before they've had time to take root.'

'Perhaps people didn't try hard enough,' said Pierre. 'Anyway, I'm going to do it, however hard I find it, and no matter how long it takes me.'

Next day Pierre went to the nearby village and bought all the young trees he could afford. He stopped at the library and came out with three large books on tree care. Then he planted the saplings, choosing the best-protected corners and packing the roots well with as much good

clay as he could scrape together. Next day he rose at dawn, crossed the valley and planted the rest of his trees on the steep slopes of the other side. From then until dusk he roamed for miles, picking up the healthiest seeds and saplings he could lay his hands on.

From then on the pattern of his life was the same every day. He rose at first light and walked all over the slopes of the valley, packing up loose earth around one plant, tearing creepers off another, and treating each one as if it were his own child. He became very proud of the sturdy little trees.

Winter came. Rain fell for three days. When Pierre got out on the fourth morning every single sapling had been uprooted and some were lost forever. He stuck them back and packed the roots with mud strengthened with stones. Next morning many of them were gone again. Pierre repaired the damage as best he could. It was a fearful winter for the young man but he didn't give up. When spring came half of his trees were standing. He worked all summer, studying the care of trees as well as planting them. Another winter brought all sorts of disasters but Pierre fought them tooth and nail. Every setback spurred him on to greater efforts.

Fifty years later Pierre, now himself a grandfather, stood on the hillside where he had made his promise so long ago. Between the thickly wooded hillsides stretched a rich green plain dotted with cattle and farm-houses. Pierre was filled with pride as he recalled what the President of France had said to him the day before as he pinned one of the country's most important medals on the old man's chest: 'You have taught all of us to struggle on when the odds seem hopeless. We have learned that when a determined man sets his mind to finishing a mighty task nothing on earth can stop him.'

Bacon and the Fishermen

(Adapted from the *Apophthegms* of Bacon)

Many years ago a great lawyer named Francis Bacon was walking beside the River Thames at Chelsea. Seeing that the fisher-men were about to put out for the day – for in those days the clean waters of the river teemed with fish – Bacon shouted down to them, 'Will you sell me all the fish you catch today?'

The fishermen turned towards a square-headed, middle-aged man, evidently their leader, who thought for some moments and then said, 'If the price is right. How much will you give us?'

It was now Bacon's turn to think. 'Ten shillings,' he said.

'You're joking,' said the fisherman. 'We may come in with a boatload of fine fish. Tell you what, offer us thirty shillings and you're on.'

'Too much,' said Bacon. 'Ten shillings is my last offer. Take it or leave it.'

'No thanks,' said the fisherman, pre-paring to cast off.

'Well, I'll stay and see how you get on,' said the lawyer, settling down on the river-bank.

The tiny fleet put out into the middle of the river and the lines were quickly cast over the sides. From where Bacon lay he could see the small figures of the fishermen going busily about their duties. After some time the captain seemed to be dissatisfied with that stretch of the river for he moved his boats upstream. A little later he brought them down again.

Bacon spent the whole day, except for an hour in a tavern, in the sunlit grass watching the fishing-boats. He enjoyed the day's holiday from work and was curious to see how many fish they would bring in.

As the sun set the boats returned to Chelsea.

'How many?' asked Bacon.

'None,' came the badtempered reply.

The lawyer threw back his head and roared with laughter. 'You should have taken my offer,' he said.

'We hoped to have a good catch,' said the fisherman.

'My friend,' said the wise lawyer, 'hope is a good breakfast but a bad supper.'

When Bacon had left the fisherman pondered what he had said. He must mean, he thought, that it is good to believe we'll succeed when we start out on an action, bad if at the end all we have is hope.

Marie Curie

Many years ago a young Polish girl named Marie Sklodovska came to study in Paris. Although she spoke very little French she was determined to study science and mathematics at the university of the Sorbonne. At first she could hardly follow the lectures there, but she applied herself to learning the language and soon spoke and wrote perfect French. She worked hard and passed her examinations with flying colours.

She was offered a scholarship which allowed her to stay another year in Paris to work on the magnetic properties of steel. She was delighted, but there was one snag. She needed a larger workroom than her own little one. Someone told her of a scientist named Pierre Curie who had a larger workroom than he needed. She asked him if she could share it and he agreed. So she moved in her equipment and set to work. It was not long before she and Pierre grew fond of each other, fell in love and married.

At this time scientists everywhere were becoming interested in radiation, that is, invisible rays which can pierce solid objects. Marie became fascinated by it and set to work to find out all about it. It took years – years of setbacks, heartbreaks, poverty and discouragement. In that time Marie gave birth to the first of her two children. She ran a home and worked long hours in the shed at the end of her garden. Her husband gave her valuable help.

At last she found what she had been searching for – radium. It was a glowing, blue metal. She knew it was important in healing, for it could kill diseased cells in the human body. She also knew that it could be deadly dangerous to healthy cells. All the same she pressed on with her experiments to find the best uses for this remarkable new metal.

Meanwhile doctors were using it to bring about wonderful cures. The world began calling for more radium. Why wasn't there more of it available for the world's hospitals, people wanted to know. Was this Madame Curie holding on to a large load to sell it at a high price? Who was she anyway? Newspaper reporters came in droves to question and re-question the hardworking couple. Marie explained that radium was very hard to make, and that she was working night and day to find ways of producing large quantities quickly. She promised that she would give the rest of her life to the study of this marvellous new stuff.

And she did. She worked on through thick and thin. She was broken-hearted when Pierre was killed in a street accident, but she soon redoubled her efforts in the laboratory. Her health grew worse, as she knew it would, for radium was slowly killing her. In those days scientists did not have the safeguards we have nowadays to prevent radium from killing the body cells. But Marie Curie knew that it was the only way to bring new hope to millions of sufferers. At last she died, the first victim of radiation sickness, and was laid to rest beside her husband.

George Washington Carver

It is hard to imagine a worse start in life than the one George Carver had. He was born the son of a Negro slave in America more than a hundred years ago. He was a sickly baby with a constant cough. One night bandits on horseback came and kidnapped his mother, sister and himself. George was found later but he never saw his mother and sister again and never knew what happened to them. He never knew who his father was.

The sickly, stammering child was brought up by the family who had 'owned' his mother. He was not strong enough to work in the fields, so the farmer's wife let him help in the kitchen. He quickly showed that he had great skill at cooking and needlework. He was also passionately interested in flowers and other plants. He brought them into the house, learned their names and took them apart to see how they grew. When he was older and able to walk greater distances from the farm he took samples of the soil and found out which type of earth each plant grew best in.

Soon George realized that in order to learn more he would have to go to school, for he could neither read nor write. The village school was open only to white children so he left home and went to another town. There the teenage boy sat in a crowded classroom for the first time, paying for his food and lessons by scrubbing clothes and washing dishes in the home of a washerwoman. He worked very hard at his books, and, because he had a brilliant mind, he quickly learned all he could in that small school.

He then walked to another town to go to a higher school but the head turned him away because he was black. Then for many years he drifted from place to place working as a farmer, cook and laundryman. At last he managed to get into a university. To pay for his lessons he started a laundry in a shack near the teaching block. Many students brought him their washing, for he was well-liked and everyone wanted to help him succeed.

And succeed he did. At the age of thirty-five he passed his final examination. He was at once offered a teaching post in the university. He took it gladly. Two years later he received his master's degree. He was now an expert on plants; he was also *Dr* Carver. He then went to teach in a school for Negro students run by Booker T. Washington who, like Carver, was the son of a slave. There he remained for the rest of his life.

Dr Carver did more than teach at the Tuskegee Institute. He studied plant life more closely than it had ever been studied before. His discoveries were remarkable. He taught farmers how they could grow more and better crops. He found hundreds of new uses for the humble peanut, from butter to a cough mixture. He taught everyone to use plants like watercress, chicory

and chickweed in soups and salads. From the sweet potato he developed more than a hundred new products including flour and the gum used on postage stamps.

The name of George Washington Carver became famous all over America. Businessmen asked him to work for them at huge salaries. Thomas Edison, the inventor of the electric light bulb and the record-player, invited him to join him at a salary of $100,000 a year. Dr. Carver refused all these offers. He just wanted to stay where he was to help his students.

However, he was determined to help not only his own people but all mankind. He gave away all his discoveries freely, for he wished to make more good cheap food available as soon as possible. He cared so little about money that he forgot to cash his pay cheques for years on end. He never asked for a rise in salary and when one was offered to him he turned it down. He didn't need money, he said. He wore the same overcoat for forty years.

His friends looked on him as a saint. He was never bitter or unkind. Although he worked all his life at a furious pace he was always willing to help anyone, however unimportant. In spite of the fact that in later life his friends included three presidents he was always simple and natural. When he died they wrote on his tombstone 'He could have added fortune to fame, but caring for neither, he found happiness and honour in being helpful to the world.'

Breaking the Bad News

Once upon a time there was a king who had a favourite horse which he dearly loved. The animal was equally fond of him and would run whinnying to him whenever he saw him. People used to say that they would rather be the king's horse than his servant, for he had a violent temper and would think nothing of ordering a man's death if he was displeased.

One day the horse fell ill. The king sent for all the best animal doctors in the land. They came, examined the horse, made tests, gave it medicine and shook their heads doubtfully. 'I am afraid, your majesty,' said one timidly, 'that there is very little hope for your pet. He is very ill and you must prepare yourself for the worst.'

'If he dies,' hissed the king, 'I shall see to it that the man who tells me of his death will die too.'

'But sire . . .' protested the doctor.

'But nothing!' roared the king. 'Whoever brings me the news of my horse's death will hang.' And off he stumped.

That night the horse died. There was panic in the palace. Who was going to tell the king? The doctors, grooms, stableboys and politicians argued and pleaded with each other but nobody could be found who was crazy enough to carry the terrible news to the king.

Finally a young army officer, on being told the story, said, ' I'll do it. Just leave it to me.'

'But you'll die,' said his friends. The young soldier simply laughed and went to see the king.

'Your majesty,' he said, 'I have come to give you news of your horse.'

'Quick, man,' said the king. 'How is he?'

'He is stretched out in his stall. He doesn't eat. He doesn't drink. He doesn't sleep. He doesn't breathe . . .'

The king rose. 'Then he is dead,' he said in a rage.

'Your majesty is right,' said the soldier, 'and you have told yourself the news. I did not tell you he was dead.'

The king laughed. 'You're a clever fellow,' he said, 'How did you come to be so smart?'

The young soldier answered, 'When I was a boy my mother taught me that I

could do great damage with my tongue and must learn to control it. Since then I have always been careful to see that nothing I say will hurt other people or myself.'

The king told him to go back to the barracks and decided he would never act so wildly again.

Operation Jericho

The doctor lay on his prison bunk and stared out at the grey sky. He had watched the tumbling snowflakes through the barred window and could imagine the yard outside covered by a white carpet. His thoughts turned to his wife and daughter. He smiled to think that they were safe and warm in their cottage in the country. Would he ever see them again? he wondered.

Dr Mans had been chief medical officer of the French city of Amiens when the Germans came early in the Second World War. Like most Frenchmen he hated being ruled by strangers. He and other doctors saved many young men from the forced labour camps by pretending they were not fit for hard work. He joined the secret group set up in the city to fight the Germans by wrecking trains, bombing factories and sending useful information to the British, who had carried on the war after the surrender of France. At last he was caught and taken to Amiens Jail, a cross-shaped building set in a wide yard bounded by a high wall. Seven hundred prisoners – all members of the underground army – crowded the cells. Many of them had no hope of leaving the jail alive. Hardly a day passed without a number being taken out and shot.

The doctor's thoughts were interrupted by a tremendous bang as a bomb exploded near the outside wall. He rushed to the window. The sound of another explosion, this time nearer, filled the air. Wild shouts rang down the corridors. A voice screamed, 'The British are bombing the jail to set us free!' It was true. The R.A.F. was carrying out a desperate plan called Operation Jericho. The idea was to knock down the walls, as Josue had done to the old city.

By now the air was filled with the zoom of low-flying planes and the noise of exploding bombs. Well-aimed hits wrecked the guards' rooms at the end of the building. The outer wall was breached in several places. Then nearer, louder crashes told that the raiders were planting their bombs close to the walls of the jail itself.

The loudest boom of all thundered in the doctor's ears. It was followed by a

mighty tearing, rolling din and a choking cloud of dust. When the uproar stopped he saw a wide gap in the inner wall of his cell. He tottered through it into the main hall. A voice from a first-floor cell shouted to him. It was Captain Tempez, a leader of the secret fighters.

'Get the keys!' he roared.

Dr Mans fetched them from the office, freed Tempez and gave him the keys. Then he made his way out to the yard. He looked around. Here and there lay the bodies of guards and prisoners, some wounded, some already dead. The muffled shouts of men trapped under piles of stones came from the jail. Near him lay a dying woman prisoner, her head cushioned in her husband's arms. Hundreds of prisoners streamed towards the gaps in the outer wall, where friends had suddenly appeared.

The doctor's mind flew to thoughts of the cottage in the country. He could see the surprise and delight on the faces of his family as he burst in and told of his escape. How wonderful it would be to live again the life of a free man and not that of a caged animal!

'No,' he said to himself, 'I can't go. I'm a doctor. I must help.'

He set to work furiously, tending the wounded – prisoners and guards alike. Soon Tempez appeared. He too refused to escape and began to clear away the rubble to free trapped men. Not long afterwards a friend came and tried to persuade the doctor to escape in his car. He shook his head and carried on treating the injured. Some time later German guards arrived. Both men were rounded up but Dr Mans insisted on going to the hospital with the wounded prisoners. The doctor's dream of home and freedom was over.

Later Dr Mans was sent to a prison camp. Many died in those dreadful places but he did not. At the end of the war he was saved from execution by the arrival of the Americans. Captain Tempez was not so lucky. He was shot at Amiens.

War is a savage business, but the doctor and the soldier who gave up their freedom to help others proved that it does not make all men savages.

St George

St George is the patron, or special, saint of England. We do not know much about his life. He was born somewhere in the Middle East, not far from where Jesus lived and died.

We are told that George was a soldier in the service of the Roman emperor about two hundred years after the time of Jesus. When he became a Christian he left the army, which at that time had been ordered to seek out and imprison all Christians. He gave away everything he owned and set out to do good works.

The best-known story about him tells of the time he came to a city which was being terrorized by a dragon. At first the citizens had kept the dragon away by feeding it with two sheep every day. When they ran out of sheep they had been forced to give it one of their young men and women every time the fearsome beast was hungry. On the day George came he found the king's daughter tied to a post, weeping, waiting to be eaten. When he learned what was happening he attacked and killed the dragon and brought her back to her father.

George explained that he had got the strength to kill the dragon only because he was a Christian. He told the people of the city all about Jesus and urged them to become Christians, which they did. He then left and had many more adventures, doing good wherever he came to rest. He was at last captured and killed by the Romans.

This is the story which was told many

years later to the English knights who went out to that part of the world to free the Christian holy places. They were struck with admiration for St George, and some of them actually believed that he had been seen to fight on their side in battle. They

66

carried his flag, which showed a red cross on a white background, and brought his story back to England. The English were so taken with the tale of St George and the dragon that they made him their special saint.

Now you may be sure that many of them did not really believe the story, but it did teach them two important lessons: first, to help those in need and second, that a person with great faith can perform wonderful deeds.

St David

St David is the special saint of Wales. The old stories tell us that he came of noble parents and that his mother was a very holy woman. He was born about fifteen hundred years ago.

He studied to become a priest under another Welsh saint. He then set out to build monasteries and built them in twelve different places. Do you know what a monastery is? It is a big building in which monks live. David was an energetic man, never happier than when he was preparing the plans for a new house. He was also a holy man, and soon stories began to go around about the miracles he was said to have performed.

At this time a number of people began to believe that Jesus never really came to live on earth in human form, that is, with real flesh and blood. They taught that he came in spirit – that the Jesus his friends saw was a kind of ghost. This way of thinking greatly shocked the chiefs of the church in Wales. They called a great meeting to let all Welsh Christians know that these ideas must be stamped out.

They chose David to be their leading speaker. He spoke so earnestly and with such force that his opponents were completely overcome. It was said that while he was speaking a white dove flew on to his shoulder and the ground rose under him until he stood on a hill-top. Now it is unlikely that this really happened. It is prob-

ably a very colourful way of saying that he spoke as if the spirit of God had come to him, and that he seemed to tower over everyone else there.

After the meeting David was made chief of the Welsh Church. This did not make any change in his way of life. He and his brother monks led a very hard life. They usually drank only water. Sometimes, if they felt like a treat, they mixed it with a little milk. They never touched meat. They spoke to each other only when it was strictly necessary. Some people say that their food consisted mainly of leeks which grew in the fields around their house.

David died at a great age on 1st March, so that is the day on which Welsh people celebrate their own saint. Their statues of St David show him standing on a hill-top with a dove on his shoulder. They have taken the leek as their special plant. His last words were 'Be joyful, brothers and sisters. Keep your faith, and do the little things that you have seen and heard with me.'

St Andrew

When John the Baptist met Jesus he knew that there was something special about him and said so. A fisherman named Andrew, a friend of John's, decided to follow Jesus to hear what he had to say. He also told his brother Simon, later called Peter, about this strange new preacher and Simon too became a follower of Jesus.

One day Jesus came along to the lake-side to find the brothers working at their nets. 'Come with me and I'll make you fishers of men,' he said, meaning that they would gather believers in Jesus's ideas as they had gathered fish in their nets. The two men left their trade at once and became the first apostles of their master.

Now everyone knows a good deal about Peter, who became the leader of the Christians after Jesus's death, but they do not give much thought to his brother Andrew. We remember that it was Andrew who told Jesus about the boy who had the loaves and fish with which he is said to have fed five thousand people. Another time some Greeks asked Philip, one of the twelve apostles, if they could speak to Jesus. Philip told Andrew and they both went to ask Jesus. This seems to show that Andrew was one of the very closest friends Jesus had.

When Jesus was killed Andrew went to foreign lands preaching the words he had heard Jesus speak. This was highly dangerous, for the Romans, who ruled all that part of the world, held that their emperor was a god and that it was wicked to worship an invisible god in the skies. Every Christian of those days knew that he might finish up hanging from a cross as Jesus did. For the leaders there was even more danger.

We are told that Andrew went from place to place without any thought for his own safety, fearlessly speaking the message he had heard from his master's own lips. At last he was taken by the Romans and crucified. They say he was fixed to an X-shaped cross so that he would take longer to die, and so suffer more. In this dreadful situation, the story goes, Andrew continued to preach to a great crowd until his life ebbed away.

Hundreds of years later the bones of St Andrew were in the care of a man named Rule. One night in a dream an angel appeared to him and told him to take the relics to Scotland. He did as he was instructed and built a church there to house the holy bones. In later years the Scots came to look on Andrew as their own special saint. They believed he helped them in battle and they looked on his flag – a white X-shaped cross on a blue background – as Scotland's own.

Every year on 30th November the Scots celebrate St Andrew's Day. At concert halls and theatres all over the country people listen to the songs, poems and plays of their land. It is strange to think that they have taken as their special saint a man who never set foot in their country and probably never even heard of it.

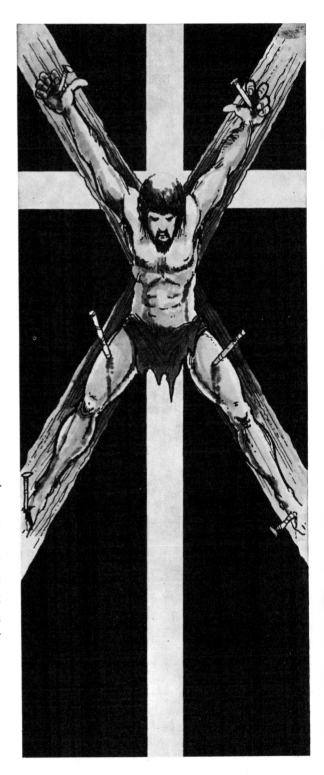

St Patrick

Many years ago the High King of Ireland sat with his nobles and their ladies in the great dining-hall of his palace. Suddenly a soldier burst into the room. 'Sire,' he said breathlessly, 'someone has lit a fire.'

There was a shocked silence. This was Easter time when the king, advised by his wizards, had ordered that no fire should be lit before his own. Anyone who disobeyed this order was to be put to death.

'Fetch the rascal at once,' ordered the king.

The soldier ran out and gathered a party of the king's guards. In a short time they were back, pushing their prisoners before them. There were twelve of them, dressed in curious gowns tied with a cord at the waist. The king thought they looked harmless enough.

'You have lit a fire at this sacred time,' he said, 'the penalty for which is death. Did you know this?'

'Yes,' answered their leader, a mild, grey-haired man. 'We knew what we were doing and we did it in order to speak to you.'

The king laughed. 'Well, say what you have to before we put you to death. You've earned your few words.'

So the strange priest – for that is what he was – told his story. His name was Patrick, he said. He had been born in a foreign country but stolen from his parents when a child by Irish pirates. He spent

many years as a shepherd boy on the Irish hills before he managed to escape. He got back home and became a priest of the Christian faith. He travelled in many lands but could not forget the Irish, whom he loved. They knew nothing of Jesus and the wonderful new ideas he had spread. He made up his mind to come to Ireland and teach the people to be Christians. He landed at Easter, heard about the order not to light a fire, and deliberately broke it. And here he was.

'Who is this Jesus you keep mentioning?' asked the king.

Patrick told the story of Jesus's life from beginning to end. Then he explained his teachings, so different from the magical beliefs which the king had held from his childhood. He found Patrick's talk so interesting that he said he would allow him to live until the next day, as he still wanted to ask him a few questions about this strange new religion. Patrick and his friends were flung in the cells and the king went to bed.

Next day Patrick was fetched to walk with his royal questioner on the lawn in front of the castle. The priest talked, argued, explained and contradicted so skilfully that the king came to believe that this might indeed be the true religion.

'One thing bothers me,' said the king. 'It's this idea that there is one god, but that he is made up of three persons. That baffles me. How can you have three persons in one god?'

Patrick bent and picked up a tiny, three-leafed plant. 'Look at this shamrock,' he said. 'It has three leaves. Yet there is only one plant. In the same way there are three persons in one god.'

The king was so struck with this clever way of putting over the idea that he said he doubted no more and wanted to become a Christian. Patrick baptized him and many of his nobles.

Soon afterwards, with the good wishes of the king ringing in his ears, Patrick set out to make Ireland a Christian country. It was a dangerous task. Travelling about some of the wilder parts of the country meant risking attack by the bandits there. It was dangerous also to preach a new religion to men who hated what was strange, and were not above killing to silence those they disagreed with. Patrick knew all these difficulties and faced them without fear.

For thirty years Patrick and his friends travelled the length and breadth of Ireland preaching, baptizing and building churches. At the end of that time Patrick, by now near death, had done what he set out to do. Ireland was Christian. She has remained so ever since.

So every year on 17th March, the anniversary of Patrick's death, Irish children put on their best clothes and lots of them pin a little bunch of shamrocks to their jackets and dresses. Then they go to church to sing hymns and listen to sermons praising their saint.

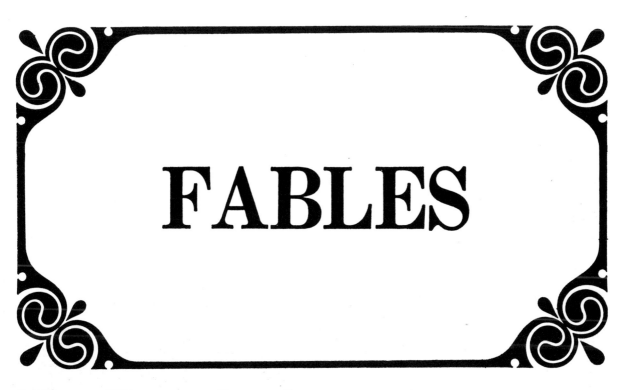

FABLES

The Bear in the Quicksands

One day a bear was walking on the sands. He had never been to that part of the country before and, as he looked around, he thought how lucky were the animals who lived there. They had a long, wide patch of sand to walk on – a patch provided by a tide which went out a long way.

Suddenly he felt his feet sink into the sand. He tried to pull them out but the more he tugged the deeper he sank. Quicksands, he thought. I've heard of them – sands that shift and suck you down – but I've never seen them. He squirmed and struggled, but it was no good. Slowly but surely he began to be drawn into the sand.

He quickly realized that his only chance of saving his life was to get help. He threw back his great head and roared ' He-e-e-lp!' A monkey appeared on the nearest dry hummock almost at once.

' For pity's sake help me!' moaned the bear.

' I'm not sure whether you deserve any help,' chattered the monkey. ' After all, you know that there are such things as shifting sands, and you know that they are more common in places where the tide goes out a long way. Besides, you're not from around these parts so you should have had enough sense to be extra careful. You've landed in this mess through your own foolishness. Do you know what I think?' And the monkey continued to scold the bear at the top of his voice.

Meanwhile an owl had come up. 'What's the matter?' he wanted to know.

'Please get me out of these quicksands,' begged the bear.

'I don't think anything can be done to help you, my poor friend,' said the owl. 'My advice is to face the fact that your end has come, as it must come to all of us. You must accept it bravely, if possible with a smile on your lips. If you would like to speak a last few courageous words we will report them to your friends – perhaps to your father bear, or mother bear, or possibly your little baby bears. But there are two things you must remember when facing death.' And the owl proceeded to tell him at great length what the two things were.

Next thing, a beaver showed up beside

the owl. 'What's all this?' he asked.

'For heaven's sake help me,' begged the bear, by now up to his waist in sand.

Without a word the beaver turned and scuttled up a tree. With half a dozen slashes of his razor-sharp teeth he had cut through a trailing climbing plant, the sort that Tarzan swings on. It fell to the ground and the beaver was after it in a flash. Swiftly he tied it round the base of the tree. Then, taking the loose end in his mouth, he crawled out to the bear. 'Hold on to this

74

and pull with all your might,' he ordered. The bear did as he was told while the beaver sped back to dry land to haul from that end.

What a tremendous tugging and puffing then began! The bear flexed his giant muscles and strained till he thought his heart would burst. The beaver, who knew what hard work was all about, felt that this was one battle he was going to lose. But slowly, painfully, the bear managed to drag himself free of the great hole. Spreading out his big body he hauled with all his strength, helped by the encouraging tugging and shouting of the beaver. After a deal of sweat and effort the bear managed to pull himself to the green bank.

When he had got his breath back he thanked the beaver with tears in his eyes for having saved his life. Then he turned to the owl and the monkey. 'And thank you very much,' he said bitterly. 'If I'd been depending on you two for help I'd be lying under ten or twenty feet of sand now as dead as a doornail.' He shambled off in disgust.

'Gentlemen,' said the beaver when the bear had gone, 'when somebody is in trouble don't talk. Act.'

The Fowler and the Quails

Do you know what a fowler – f-o-w-l-e-r – is? No, he's not a bad footballer. A fowler is a man who captures birds with a net, though there are not as many of them about as there used to be. A fowler used to have a whistle on which he could imitate the song of a bird. When the real birds came to see their 'friend' he would throw the net over them, put them in his wooden cage, and carry them off to be sold at the market.

The worst sufferers were the quails which were great favourites at the tables of rich nobles. Fowlers were so keen to catch these birds that they went to any lengths. They even used to blind one and take it to the woods with them, where its pitiful cries attracted other quails, which in turn were caught.

'This has got to stop,' said the chief quail one day. 'If we don't do something we'll all soon be bones.'

'What can we do?' asked another helplessly. 'After all, when the net falls all the struggling in the world can't get us out through that fine mesh.'

'You know why?' asked the chief quail.
'Why?'

'Because we all panic when we feel the net fall on us. We go wild. All we can think of is escape. We flutter madly against it, which only gets us more firmly tangled up in it. Now here's what I suggest,' said the chief quail earnestly. The other birds gath-

wings. The net took off into the air supported by the quails, who flew joyfully to another part of the woods in formation, like a flight of aeroplanes. When they had hung the net at the top of a tall tree as a kind of trophy one said, 'We've fooled the fowler. We'll have no more trouble from him.'

Nor did they – for a time. Whenever they felt the net fall on them they acted with the well-drilled smartness of a crack squad of soldiers. Straight up into the air they flew, leaving another fowler staring in amazement as his net floated off into the blue.

However, as the days passed the quails became more and more proud and boastful. Each bird claimed that he had first thought of the new idea and that he carried the heaviest part of the net. Quarrels broke out and bitter words flew. Birds who had been friends for years fell out and stopped speaking to each other. Soon the behaviour of the quails was the talk of the woods. They were, the other creatures said, a disgrace to the animal kingdom. Even the shrews, who were known far and wide for their bad tempers, shook their heads at the antics of the foolish birds.

One day the chief quail called them together to see if they could settle their differences. Sadly the meeting became a slanging match with angry screams filling the air. At the height of the row a fowler strolled up and threw his net over them. At once their leader shouted the usual commands, but do you think they obeyed him? No, they were all too angry with each other to work together. Each one fluttered madly

ered round to hear what their leader had to say. He spoke forcefully, his bright eyes flashing as he explained his new idea. His followers listened, at first puzzled, then, as the plan became clearer, with nods and smiles. Clearly they were pleased with what they had heard.

The very next day the quails were perched in the same spot when the fowler crept without a sound towards them. Silently he edged his way through the bushes. Now he was no more than an arm's length away from the nearest bird. With a sudden expert flick he threw his net over the flock.

'Right,' shouted the chief quail, 'this is it. No panic, now! When I give the word, rise. Rise!' At that each bird calmly took the net cord in his bill and flapped his

against the cord in wild terror, concerned only with his own safety. Quickly they became entangled. In a short time the smiling fowler had filled his sack.

Only a few escaped. One was their chief, who said grimly to the others, 'Now I hope you learned your lesson. If we work together and help each other, we'll be safe. If we fall out we'll be picked off easily. Have you got that?' He looked round the ring of frightened faces. They nodded. They knew – now.

Brer Rabbit, the Elephant and the Whale

'Yes,' said the elephant to Brer Rabbit, 'I don't think anyone would deny that I am the strongest creature on earth. Look how big I am.' And he drew himself up to his full height and raised his trunk in the air like a boxer who has just scored a knockout. 'I hope you don't think I'm boasting,' he went on. 'If you're as powerful as I am you can't help knowing it, any more than if you're a timid, feeble creature like you you can avoid knowing it.' He laughed unpleasantly.

Brer Rabbit laughed too, but he was not amused. 'My friend, don't be misled by your size,' he said. 'I know you can do a few party tricks like tearing up a tree by the roots, but you have no real strength – nothing to compare with my mighty muscles.' He sat up on his hind legs and drew in a deep breath to swell his tiny chest.

The elephant laughed so hard that he had to lean against a tree to save himself from falling. 'Your mighty muscles!' he choked. 'Oh dear, what a little comic you are!'

'I'm deadly serious,' said Brer Rabbit, 'and I'll prove it. Let's have a tug-o'-war. You take one end of this rope and I'll take the other. We'll see who can pull hardest.'

'This is ridiculous,' said the elephant,

'but I'll do it anyway. It'll teach you a lesson, you foolish little thing.'

Brer Rabbit tied the end of a long rope around the elephant's waist. 'Now I'll take the other end down on to the sands, through those bushes,' said Brer Rabbit. 'When I shout "Pull" do your worst.' The elephant agreed, Brer Rabbit tied the rope round him, and went off through the bushes on to the beach.

Not far out in the water a whale was sunning himself. 'Hello,' shouted Brer Rabbit, 'wasn't it you who told me yesterday that you were the strongest creature on earth?'

'It was,' answered the whale, 'but I don't suppose it was any news to you. I believe it's widely known.'

'I think I'm stronger than you,' said Brer Rabbit, 'and I'm ready to prove it. Let's have a tug-o'-war to see who's the tougher. I'll tie this rope around your waist and take the other end through the bushes up on to the grass. When I shout "Pull" pull. Okay?'

'Okay,' said the whale, hardly able to believe what he heard. Brer Rabbit tied the end of the rope round the great middle of the whale and went back up into the bushes. Once there he could not keep him-

self from laughing at the idea of the elephant at one end of the rope and the whale at the other. Then he shouted, 'Pull.'

The elephant gave a gentle tug. Nothing happened. He planted his great feet in the grass and gave a hefty pull. The whale was yanked his own length through the water.

'Cor!' he said, 'This little bloke isn't as feeble as he looks. I'll have to teach him a lesson.' With a powerful thrashing of his mighty tail he headed out to sea. The elephant found himself dragged off his feet and sliding along the grass on his bottom. He managed to slither to his feet and dug them into the ground to avoid being pulled into the sea. Then slowly he inched his way back from the bushes, where Brer Rabbit was lying chuckling at the groans and grunts of the two sweating giants. The whale felt himself slipping back towards the shore. He too exerted all his enormous strength. The great beasts strained at the rope until each was on the verge of collapse.

Brer Rabbit saw his chance. He shouted to the elephant, 'I could keep this up all day. Do you want to give up?'

'Yes,' gasped the elephant, falling gratefully on the grass.

Brer Rabbit turned towards the sea. 'Want to give up?' he shouted.

'I surrender,' panted the whale, as he sank to the bottom for a rest. As Brer Rabbit untied the rope from the defeated beasts he had the same message for each: 'Pride comes before a fall and boasting is always punished.'

The Woodcock and the Fox

One day a hungry fox was walking in the forest when he saw a woodcock sitting on the branch of a tree. It was a fine bird, plump and well-developed. The fox's mouth watered at the sight.

'Hello, friend,' he said with a pleasant smile. 'When I saw you I said to myself, " I must go along and see how that handsome bird is getting along." I hope your health is good.'

'I'm very well,' replied the woodcock, 'and I'm grateful to you for asking.'

'What was that you said?' asked the fox. 'I'm sorry, but I'm slightly deaf and can't hear you very well. Why not come down here on the grass and we can have a nice chat?'

'I said I felt fine,' said the woodcock loudly, 'and if you don't mind I'd rather stay up here. You see, I'm a bit nervous in case I'm attacked by an animal. You know, there are some creatures who would just love to get their teeth into a big bird like me.'

'Do you tell me that?' said the fox with a shocked expression.

'It's a fact,' said the woodcock.

'Still, it seems a pity that you can't come down, if only for a few minutes,' said the fox. 'You see, I've always been told what a beautiful bird you are, but my eyesight isn't what it used to be and I can't

been for this law you would have been torn to pieces. As it is you can stay here and chat quite safely.'

The fox was off like a streak of lightning. Later the woodcock said to his children, 'Of course I knew from the beginning what he was after and I made up the bit about the dogs to frighten the life out of the rascal. But remember this, children. When someone says as many pleasing things to you as the fox said to me be on your guard. Those who love us best don't always speak mostly kindly to us.'

see the full range of your colourful plumage from here. I hear that the way your brown, red and black feathers blend is really something to see at close range. Won't you come down for a minute or two to let me admire you?'

The woodcock looked pleased and seemed in two minds about what to do. Then he said, 'No, perhaps not. In the few moments I would spend down there a hungry creature could rush out from behind a tree and make off with me in his mouth. No, I think I'm safer up here.'

The fox said, 'Oh, I forgot to tell you. All the animals have had a great meeting and passed a law forbidding any creature to attack any other. We're all to live at peace with each other. So you're quite safe to come down.'

'I'm glad to hear that,' said the woodcock, 'for your sake.'

'For my sake?' asked the fox, puzzled.

'Yes,' said the woodcock. 'You see, from up here I can see a pack of hounds heading straight for this spot. If it hadn't

The Fox's Trial

So many stories were being told about the wickedness of the fox that all the animals decided that he must be brought to trial. So they took him before the lion, who sat in the middle of the great circle of beasts and said, 'Call the first witness.'

'I'm the first witness,' said the eagle. 'We have all heard these dreadful tales so I won't horrify the younger animals by repeating them. What shocks me about them, what really sticks in my craw, is that he attacks only creatures which have no chance against him – small defenceless animals like hens and rabbits. If he had ever tackled one as big as himself I think it might be possible to forgive him, but he hasn't. I find him disgusting.'

The lion nodded. 'Thank you, Mr Eagle,' he said. 'Who is the next to give evidence?'

'I am,' said the spider. 'I agree with every word Brother Eagle has said, but I should like to draw the court's attention to an even nastier side of the prisoner's character – I mean his low cunning. We have all heard stories of his crafty plotting, of his cowardly attacks under cover of darkness. It is this sly, underhand behaviour that makes me say we ought to get rid of him.'

The lion said, 'Thank you, Mr Spider. Call the next witness.'

'I'm the last witness for the prosecution,' said the cheetah. 'I shall only draw your attention to the fact that the fox kills only creatures which are much slower than he is. When you think of how much faster he can run than chickens or poor waddling ducks and geese it's enough to make your blood boil. I can understand a fair chase and a kill where the hunted animal has some chance of escaping, but a race between a goose and a fox. . .' and the cheetah shook his head in shocked disapproval.

'Is that the end of the case for the prosecution?' asked the lion.

'It is,' replied the owl.

'Well,' said the lion, 'I have no doubt that all we have heard about the fox is true. The eagle accuses him of attacking only animals which are weaker than he is. We will take the eagle's word for this, for he's an expert on attacking feeble creatures. He does it all the time.

'The spider tells us that the cunning fox lies in wait for his victims, having set traps for them. I believe him, for nobody knows more about weaving crafty plots than the spider who kills his victims that way.

'Lastly, the cheetah complains that the fox's speed makes his hunting unfair. This may be so, but it sounds strange coming from the fastest of all animals.

'Gentlemen, you remind me of the humans, who, when they wish to scold one of their number, always accuse him of their own worst fault. The thieves find him dishonest, the liars complain that he's untruthful, the bullies call him a bully and so on. Now I don't like the fox any more than the rest of you but I'm not going to find him guilty on the say-so of people who show the same nasty habits as he does. Case dismissed.'

The fox was set free and the animals went away rather more thoughtful than they had come.

The Fish God

Far away in India, on the banks of a great river, lived a poor fisherman named Gopal and his wife Nataki. They had a very hard life, for the few fish that Gopal caught fetched little money at the market. Their home was a miserable mud-walled hut with only half a dozen bits of furniture.

One morning when Gopal pulled in his net he found only one small fish. He was about to pick it up when to his amazement it spoke.

'Please don't harm me,' it said. 'I am the Fish God. Put me back into the river.' Gopal was so scared that he did so at once.

When the fisherman went home and told Nataki what had happened she was angry. 'You should have held him,' she said, 'and made him grant you a wish. Then I could have had some rings and ornaments for a change.'

To get away from her sharp tongue Gopal went down to the river. He sat on a tree-stump and buried his face in his hands. He thought of the unhappy life he led. Suddenly someone spoke to him. He looked up and saw the strangest figure. From the waist up he was clearly a god, with shining body and golden crown. His lower half was covered in fishy scales which ended in a forked tail.

'I am the Fish God,' said this remarkable person. 'Is there anything I can do to make you happy?'

'There is,' said Gopal eagerly. 'Could I have a golden ring for my dear wife? Oh, and I'd like some ornaments for her.'

On her finger glittered a gold ring. Pretty brooches gleamed on her sari. Gopal told her what had happened and Nataki said, 'Thanks to the Fish God I shall be happy from now on.'

And so she was – for a while. Then one day she said, 'You know, if you had been thinking sensibly that day you spoke to the Fish God we could have been much better off. Why didn't you ask for something more valuable than a few bracelets? Go back to where you saw him and try again. If he appears tell him I should like some servants to do all my work. In that way I shall make a great impression on all the people of the village. Off you go!'

Gopal went to the river and sat on the tree-stump. At once the Fish God stood before him. 'Is there anything I can do for you?' he asked.

'Yes,' said Gopal. 'Please give me six servants to help us do all the hard work.'

'Certainly,' said the Fish God. 'But I must warn you not to become too greedy.'

When Gopal arrived home he was pleased to see six strong servants busily doing the household tasks. Nataki was delighted. 'I'll never be unhappy again,' she said.

Not only did the servants do the house-work but they went fishing with Gopal. They soon became expert fishermen, with the result that Gopal's catches got bigger and bigger. He made much more money in the market, and within a short time the young couple had become the richest family in the village.

One day Nataki said, 'What a pity you didn't ask for more. I know we are well

'It shall be done,' said the Fish God. 'But remember not to be too greedy.'

When Gopal got home there stood Nataki with a delighted smile on her face.

enough off now, but we could have been even richer. Do something for me. Go and see if you can speak to the Fish God again. Ask him if I can become a princess. Think of how marvellous it would be to live in a palace, with everything you needed to make you happy, looked up to by all the common people.'

Gopal sighed and set off for the river. Once again the Fish God appeared. Once again he asked if he could help the fisherman. 'I hope so,' said Gopal. 'My wife would like to be a princess, with all the riches that go with that high position.'

'No,' was the answer. 'I tried to warn you against greed but you did not heed me. The more I gave you the more you wanted. Now I shall take everything away again. Your wife must find out that happiness is not to be found in riches and palaces only, but also in hard work.' The Fish God vanished.

On coming home Gopal found that Nataki's rings, ornaments and servants had all disappeared. His wife was in tears at the turn things had taken. Life, she thought, would be miserable without her luxuries. She couldn't face the old times of pinching and scraping. She could see nothing but drudgery ahead. Gopal tried to comfort her by telling her what the Fish God had said.

So they settled down to take up the threads of their old life. Strangely enough they found it quite easy, now that they had given up their dreams of wealth and importance. They found happiness, as the Fish God had said they would, in their hard work.

The Miller, his Son and the Donkey

(*Adapted from Aesop*)

Once upon a time a farmer set out for market with his donkey, which he hoped to sell. He took his son to keep him company. The donkey walked ahead followed by the two humans. At the corner of the street a woman called out, 'Why are you both walking when your son could be riding on the donkey? Use your brains, man.' The farmer quickly put his son on the beast's back and continued on his way, walking behind the donkey.

At the crossroads several old men were gossiping in the sunshine. 'Disgusting!' said one. 'Look at that boy riding while his poor father has to walk. Young people have no consideration nowadays. Now when I was a boy . . .' and he continued like this for another hour. But the farmer did not wait to listen. He hastily told his son to get down and walk, and he mounted the donkey. He felt better now.

Where the road neared the stream two women were approaching, carrying bags of washing. 'Good heavens!' said one. 'Look at that man riding on the donkey while the poor boy trails along behind. Isn't it a shame?' The other agreed.

'Get up behind me,' said the farmer to his son. The boy did so and the two rode on towards the market.

Next they met a gang of boys who waited until they had passed and then shouted after them, 'Monsters! Why do you load the poor creature like that? You two could just as easily carry the donkey.'

As soon as he had turned the corner the farmer dismounted and ordered his son to do the same. He made the animal lie down and tied its legs together. Next he got a long pole and placed it lengthwise between its legs. Then the farmer hoisted one end of the pole on to his shoulder and the boy did the same with the other end. Between them the donkey dangled, upside-down. Off they went, carrying the helpless animal. It was backbreaking work and they staggered from side to side. When they came to the bridge the farmer lost his footing and fell. The donkey slipped into the water and was drowned.

As he walked home the farmer said bitterly, 'From now on I'll make up my own mind what is right and do it, no matter what anyone says. I've found out once and for all that by trying to please everyone we please no-one.'

Discontented Pig

The story goes that in the old times when animals could talk there was a pig who lived alone in a cottage near the village. He was a keen gardener. Every day, whatever the weather, he could be seen digging and weeding, hoeing and planting. He was skilful as well as energetic. Every year at the vegetable shows his plants carried off the first prizes.

After some years the pig got tired of all the hard work involved in growing vegetables. 'There must be an easier way of earning a living,' he said to himself. So he locked up his house and set off to find a better job.

Soon he came to a pretty cottage from which the sounds of sweet music floated on the air. The musician was Thomas, a cat who made a good living by playing the violin.

'Will you teach me to play?' asked the pig. 'Being a musician must be easier than my tiresome job.'

'Certainly,' said the good-natured cat. 'Take my bow and fiddle and do as you've seen me do.' The pig took the instrument and began to play. The violin squeaked like a door with rusty hinges.

'Don't be discouraged,' said Thomas. 'All you need is about five hours' practice a day for a few years and you'll have the makings of a violinist.'

'Five hours a day!' exclaimed the pig. 'No thank you, my musical career has just ended. Goodbye.' And off he went.

Next he came to the cabin of a dog who made cheese. The pig looked in at the window and saw the dog pushing a pole up and down in a churn full of milk. 'That looks pretty easy,' he said to himself. He asked the dog to teach him and the dog said he was willing to try. 'Take this pole and keep squeezing up and down until the cheese is formed,' the dog told him.

The pig began with great energy but after a while his arms became very tired and he stopped to rest.

'Don't stop,' cried the dog, 'or you'll spoil the cheese. You can't take a rest until the cheese is made.'

'I can't lift my arms!' gasped the pig. 'I think I'll give up this job right away. Goodbye.' Off he went once again.

Next he saw a bee-keeper taking honey out of his beehives. It seemed such a pleasant life – all he appeared to be doing was pick up dollops of delicious honey – that the pig made up his mind on the spot that he would become a bee-keeper.

'Will you teach me your trade?' he asked.

'Of course,' the man replied. 'Here, put on these gloves and the veil. Now pick up that honeycomb.'

The pig bent down carefully. The bees crept inside his veil and gloves. They stung him viciously all over his hands and face. He roared with pain and ran away as fast as his legs would carry him.

'Come back,' shouted the man. 'Anyone who wants to be a bee-keeper must put up with a few stings.'

'Not me,' said the pig. 'I've had bee-keeping, thank you.' He carried on running until he was well away from the bees. Then, as he slowed down to a walk, he said to himself, 'Well, I've tried three jobs and found them all too hard – much more difficult than growing vegetables, which I do well. I've been a bit of a fool, but I know what I must do now.'

He went back to his cottage and unlocked his house. An hour later he was back among his vegetables, working contentedly.

Ungrateful Crocodile

Far away in India a holy man was walking along the bed of a dried-up river. He spied a crocodile panting for breath on the hot earth.

'Please save me,' gasped the crocodile. 'Take me to a river or I'll soon die. Please.'

The holy man, whose name was Astika, said, 'I'd like to save you but I've heard that you are fierce and not to be trusted. How do I know you won't attack me when I take you to safety?'

The beast looked hurt. 'Do you really think I would attack the person who had saved my life?' he asked. 'Does it seem likely? Is there a creature on the surface of the earth that would sink so low? No, my friend, if you let me live I'll bless your name until my dying day.' And a great crocodile tear rolled down his face.

Astika was so touched by this speech that he picked up the crocodile, put him in his bag, and tramped seven miles to the nearest river. Then he put him on the ground and told him to crawl down to the water.

'Please carry me into the river,' said the crocodile. 'I'm so weak I can't walk.'

Astika picked him up again, carried him into the water, and let him go. The crocodile at once seized his leg and began to drag him under.

'Rascal!' roared Astika, 'You have broken your word. Look, let's ask this passing jackal whether you are right to eat me or not. If he says that you should I'll go to my death quietly.' The crocodile grumbled a little but then agreed to ask the jackal, which is a kind of wild dog.

When the jackal had heard the full story he scratched his head and said, 'Forgive me, but I'm not very bright. Can you show me how Astika brought the creature to the river? I couldn't follow that bit.' The crocodile, tut-tutting at the jackal's stupidity, climbed into the bag and Astika tied the knot at the top.

'Take him back,' said the jackal, 'and dump him in the dried-up river where you found him.'

Astika laughed. 'Well, you are a clever bloke,' he said. 'But what a villain he is! I saved his life and he tried to take mine. Who would have thought that anyone could be so ungrateful? Who would have believed it?'

'Nearly everybody!' answered the jackal. 'My dear Astika, you are too simple, too trusting, for your own good. Carry on being kind in the future as you have in the past. But don't expect that if you do good to rogues they will be kind to you in return. It doesn't always work out that way.' Astika was forced to admit that the jackal was right.

The Wolf and the Lamb

(Adapted from La Fontaine)

One morning a wolf was drinking at a stream when, looking up, he saw a plump lamb drinking a little way downstream. He moved quietly up behind the little creature and snarled, 'Good morning, breakfast.'

'Are you going to eat me?' asked the terrified lamb.

'Indeed I am,' said the wolf, showing all his pointed teeth in a wicked smile.

'Please don't,' pleaded the lamb. 'After all, I've never done you any harm.'

'Never done me any harm!' exclaimed the wolf. 'What about last winter? What about the day you hid behind the hedge and shouted, "Who's afraid of the big, bad wolf?"'

'But I wasn't even born last winter!' said the lamb. 'You can see that I'm only a few weeks old.'

'It was your brother,' said the wolf. 'He looked exactly like you – two ears, a fluffy coat, four legs, the lot. Yes, I'm sure it was your brother.'

'But I haven't got a brother. I'm the first-born lamb in our family. Look, you have no real reason to hurt me. I've never offended you in any way.'

The wolf thought for a moment and then said, 'What about just now? You were drinking from the same water as I was. You had your dirty little snout in my drinking water.'

'You forget,' said the lamb, 'that I was drinking downstream from you. The water around my mouth was flowing away from, not towards, you.'

'Hmm,' said the wolf. 'But I'm going to eat you all the same.'

'Why?' implored the lamb. 'Give me one good reason why you should eat me.'

The wolf thought long and seriously. Then he said, 'I've got it! You wrecked my new home the other day.'

'How?' asked the lamb in amazement.

'You were running about so much that your paws caused a small earthquake and the bank fell in on my new house.'

'You don't really believe that!' the lamb gasped.

'I certainly do,' said the wolf, and without another word he scoffed down the unfortunate lamb.

When they told the wise old owl about it she said, 'Of course the villain didn't believe a word he was saying. He was only looking for an excuse. So remember, children,' she said to her owlets, 'that when you find yourself looking around for reasons for doing something that will cause pain to others you may be acting like the wolf that ate the lamb.'

The Handsomest Creature

In the old days when, we are told, the animals were able to talk, they used to meet every week in the forest for a chat. One day the peacock asked the assembly which of all the creatures of the forest they thought the handsomest. He blushed as he asked the question, for he had no doubt what their answer would be. After a short silence the hippopotamus was the first to speak.

'Ladies and gentlemen,' he said with an air of great learning, 'this is a question to which I have given a lot of serious thought. Which is the handsomest creature? Well, we can leave out all the small animals and birds; they may be pretty, perhaps, but handsome, no. To be handsome an animal must be large, with long, flowing lines that can be seen from a distance. It must have bulk and, and majesty. In short, my friends – and I hope you won't think me bigheaded if I say so – it must be the hippopotamus.'

This was greeted with laughter, jeers and groans. The rhinoceros broke into the din by saying, 'Yes, we all know that the hippo is far from good looking, but there is something in what he says. He's right when he says that to be really attractive an animal must be big enough to fill the eye. So we can rule out all the tiny fellows. But the most handsome of us must have a fine face, for it is by the face that we judge these things. Now I think you'll agree that to be handsome a face needs something special, some well-developed feature like, for example, the horn of my own kind. So after long thought I have decided in all modesty that the rhinoceros is the most beautiful.'

All the other animals hooted with laughter at this amazing claim. Next to speak was the peacock, who had only raised the question in the hope of hearing some nice things about his own appearance. He said in a furious voice, 'I really am annoyed. I thought we were going to have a sensible discussion about a serious matter. Instead we've had ridiculous bragging from the two ugliest specimens in the animal kingdom. Now I shouldn't dream of saying outright which of us is the most pleasing to look at. Perhaps that decision is best left to you. I will say that you should dismiss from your minds the lumbering heavyweights and ask yourselves, "Which of us moves most gracefully and has the most beautiful colouring?"' With that the peacock displayed his magnificent tail-feathers and walked up and down a little in his most elegant manner.

The forest creatures howled so loudly at this that the lion had to pull out an extra-special roar to silence them. 'Let us listen to the owl's opinion,' he said. 'We've all heard how wise he is, and he is sure to settle the problem for us.'

The owl broke the silence that followed by saying, 'You know, you animals remind me of the humans; although they all seem equally cruel and conceited to us, each of them feels better than others who do not live in the same country, or live in a smaller house, or are taller or shorter or darker or paler or different from themselves in any tiny way. By the same way of thinking these foolish creatures each thinks himself the most beautiful – the hippo through his size, the rhino by his horn, and the peacock because of his feathers. The truth is that there is no most handsome creature. Each animal sees that there are good looking and ugly members of his own kind – handsome and ugly hippos, rhinos and peacocks. So the question is foolish and impossible to answer.'

All the animals agreed that this was a wise speech and were about to go on to some other topic when the owl added, 'Mind you, if we *had* to choose a best-looking creature I think we should be bound to pick the one with the most pleasing face. I also feel that we should pay special attention to the eyes, which are the most important things in any face. Now we owls have remarkably bright and beautiful eyes, set off by this circular arrangement of feathers. So if I were *forced* to decide I should in all honesty choose. . . .' But at this point the owl stopped, for all the other creatures had gone off in disgust.

STORIES FROM SACRED BOOKS

The Successful Smuggler

Perhaps of all the great religions that of the Sufis is the merriest. Their wise men teach their followers by means of stories, many of which are very funny. Behind each of these ' jokes ', the Sufis say, lies an important truth. The best ones tell the comic adventures of Nasrudin, a smart-Aleck and a Jack-of-all-trades.

Nasrudin once became a smuggler. Everyone in the village knew that he was taking forbidden goods over the border and selling them at a profit in the neighbouring country. He bought a bigger house. His wife began to dress in silk. Jewels glittered on her fingers. When his friends twitted him about it he laughed and said nothing, but did not deny it. The puzzle was – what was he smuggling? None of his family knew and Nasrudin naturally kept his mouth shut. Most baffled of all was the customs officer. He knew neither what the rascal was smuggling nor how he did it. He would have given his pension to catch that smiling trickster.

Every sunrise Nasrudin jogged up to the customs post on the back of a donkey. Over the animal's back he had slung two leather bags, or panniers. The officer stopped him, made him dismount and searched the panniers. They were always full of straw. He took it out and ran expert fingers through it. Nothing. Sometimes he burned it. The ashes held no secret. Several times he cut the leather into small pieces, but with no success. Next he searched the grinning rogue from top to toe. His clothes showed nothing. Neither did his ears, nostrils, mouth or the spaces between his toes. Finally the officer would wave him on in disgust and Nasrudin would take the mountain road across the border.

In the evening the customs man waited for him. Just as the sun sank behind the hills the joker appeared over the ridge, on foot this time, and looking well pleased with himself. Next came the same careful search, with the same old result. The officer never found a thing. Often, as he watched Nasrudin stride out towards the village, he thought he saw his shoulders shake with silent laughter. The puzzled man scratched his grey head and swore that some day he would toss the villain into a prison cell.

But he never did. Nasrudin, now a rich man, gave up the game and settled down to enjoy his wealth. Not long after, the officer retired from the service. His first action after handing in his uniform was to go and see Nasrudin.

'Now that we're both retired,' he said, ' you can safely tell me how you worked it. For my own peace of mind I must know. First of all, what were you smuggling?'

'Donkeys,' was the answer.

The Sufi teachers tell us that there is a sharp lesson to be learned from this story. All the great truths, they say, are right under our noses, just like Nasrudin's donkeys. We can learn them at our mother's knee or from a friend or by simply being wide awake in our everyday lives. By chasing far-out ideas we can overlook facts that are staring us in the face.

Alexander and Katzya

(Adapted from the Talmud)

Alexander the Great, who ruled over many lands, once went to visit a king named Katzya. 'I've come,' he announced after Katzya had made him welcome, 'to see some of the customs of your country and to see if I can learn how to rule more wisely over my wide empire. I'm especially interested in your laws and how they work.'

'You couldn't have come at a better time,' said Katzya, 'for I was about to go into my judgment hall to settle a dispute. Perhaps you would like to come with me and see how I try to apply the law fairly.'

'Delighted,' said Alexander, and he went into the courtroom and sat behind the king's throne.

The two farmers who had fallen out came forward. The first said, 'Sire, I bought from this man a field in which there was a scrap-heap. It was understood that the contents of this heap were to be mine. It seemed to be made up of the usual odds and ends, but when I searched it I found a bundle of coins of great value. I believe that this treasure is mine, as it was part of the scrap-heap for which I paid the price he asked.'

'Nonsense!' said the other man. 'I sold the field and heap for a fair market price. The bundle of coins, which I did not know was there, was something more, something extra to the sale. I now ask you

to make this man return the coins to me or pay me their value.'

Katzya thought for a few minutes. Then he said to the first man, 'Have you a son?'

'Yes,' said the man with a puzzled frown.

'And you,' said the king to the second farmer, 'have you a daughter?'

'I have,' was the reply.

'That's fine,' said the king. 'You must persuade the two young people to marry. They are to have the treasure.'

When the two men had left, well satisfied, Katzya heard Alexander laughing at what he had just seen and heard. 'Why are you laughing?' he asked. 'Don't you think I judged wisely? Tell me, what would you have done if you had been in my place?'

'I should have put them both to death and taken the treasure for myself.'

'Are you really so fond of gold as all that?' asked Katzya, with a wondering shake of his head.

That night Alexander sat down to a great feast, prepared by Katzya in his honour. The emperor cheerfully took his knife to cut himself a tasty slice of chicken, but found that the knife could not pierce the bird. It was made of gold.

'What's the meaning of this?' asked Alexander angrily. 'I can't eat gold.'

'I'm sorry,' said Katzya, smiling sweetly, 'I thought you loved it so much that you could eat it. Tell me, does the sun shine in your country?'

'Naturally,' said Alexander.

'Does the rain fall?' asked Katzya.

'Of course.'

'Do you have cows there?'

'Certainly.'

'Well then, you have everything a man needs to keep him alive. The sun and rain ripen his vegetables and the cows give him their milk and meat. Try to remember, Alexander, that although you are a great emperor, you owe your life to humble animals and the produce of the land. You can't eat gold, as you said.'

Let us hope that when Alexander went back to his own country he remembered the two lessons Katzya taught him – that he must try to be fair and gentle and that like everyone else he owed his life to animals and vegetables.

David and Goliath

The two armies, arranged in battle order on opposite slopes of the valley, waited for the bugle-call to attack. The sun glittered on spears and brass helmets. Many Israelites were on their knees, offering a last-minute prayer for victory over their old enemies, the Philistines.

Suddenly there was a stir in the front ranks of the Philistines and out strode a huge man towards the Israelite lines. He stopped at the stream that cut through the valley, separating the armies. 'My name is Goliath,' he roared. 'You can save much bloodshed by sending out your best man to fight me in single combat. If he beats me, we Philistines will be your servants. If I win, your people will serve us.'

The Israelites stared fearfully at this giant of a man. The bony face, scarred in a hundred battles, the hairy, muscular forearms as thick as an ordinary man's legs, the mighty tree-trunk of a body all sent a thrill of terror through hardened soldiers. Goliath waited for an answer to his challenge. There was an angry stirring among the Israelites. Heads turned towards their best fighters. Not one moved.

With a contemptuous smile Goliath turned and walked back to his friends, who cheered loudly. Saul, King of the Israelites, furiously sounded the retreat and his men shuffled back to their tents, their heads bowed with shame. Next day Goliath repeated his challenge. Again not an

Israelite moved. He laughed and returned to his army. Once again the Israelites went back to their tents full of despair.

Goliath repeated his action for forty days without getting a single reply. On the forty-first the ranks of the Israelites parted and a teenage boy walked towards the towering warrior. He wore no armour and carried only a shepherd's stick and a sling. Goliath, astonished at the sight, wondered how a shepherd-boy had come to challenge so great a fighter as himself.

It was a strange story. The boy's name was David, and that very morning he had been about to set off for the hill to mind his father's sheep. His father had kept him at home when the war broke out but his

95

older brothers were in King Saul's army.

'No, don't go to the hill today,' his father had said, 'I want you to take this basket of food to the army. Give it to your brothers and see if they're all right.'

David set off and soon reached the valley where the two armies glared at each other across the stream. He quickly found his brothers and gave them all the news of home. They in turn told him all their war news, including the daily challenge of the Philistine giant.

'You mean no Israelite will fight him?' said David in amazement. 'Well, I'll fight him.' Off he went to King Saul's tent where he surprised everyone by repeating his offer to take on Goliath. King Saul tried to talk him out of it but it was no use. The boy had made up his mind. Saul gave him a helmet and armour but David refused to wear them, saying that he was not used to them. But he did take with him his stick and his sling – an old-fashioned catapult. David walked down to the stream under the fierce eye of Goliath. He picked up five stones worn round and smooth by the flowing water. Goliath slowly advanced. 'Come up to me,' he roared, 'and I shall give your flesh to the birds and the animals!'

David answered, 'I shall strike you and cut off your head.'

They slowly neared each other. Goliath drew his shining sword and tried some two-handed practice sweeps around his head. David put one of the stones in his sling. Then Goliath charged. At lightning speed David swung the sling three times in a circle and let go one string. The stone sped straight to Goliath's forehead and embedded itself there. A look of surprise crossed the giant's face, his mighty legs trembled and he fell dead.

Both armies stood thunderstruck. Then a mighty cheer went up from the Israelites and they charged. The Philistines, shattered by the death of their champion, ran. David, as he had promised, cut off the head of Goliath. He had shown the Israelites how to win against great odds by determination and cleverness.

Buddha and the Kings

Long ago and far away in a land called Burma two kings had a quarrel about which of them owned a piece of land crossed by a stream. They became very angry, gathered their armies and drew up their soldiers in battle order. As they were about to give the signal to charge Buddha appeared between the armies. Buddha is an Indian word which means 'wise one'. This name was given to a prince who had left his palace to find out how to live a good life. Soon many people admired his teachings and called him Buddha. His followers became known as Buddhists.

When Buddha came between the warring armies he called the kings to him. 'Tell me,' he said, 'if earth – clay – has any value of its own.'

The kings looked at each other. 'None whatever,' they answered together.

'Has water any value of its own?' asked Buddha.

'None whatever,' replied the two kings.

'And the blood of kings, has that any value of its own?' asked Buddha politely.

The kings were shocked. 'But of course,' they answered. 'The blood of kings is beyond price.'

'Well,' said Buddha, 'is it sensible to risk the precious blood of kings for a patch of mud and water?'

The two men thought it over. It did seem silly to endanger their lives and the lives of all their men for a worthless piece

of ground. Quickly they reached a simple agreement. The battle was called off. Commonsense had won.

Confucius He Say

(Adapted from the Hsiao King)

Long ago there lived a wise Chinaman named Confucius. He was so famous that many of his people followed him about to hear his sound advice on how to live good lives. He often told them how important it was to be respectful to their parents and other grownups. Young people, he said, sometimes did foolish things which they could avoid if they listened to their parents. Obedience to their father and mother was one of the surest ways of keeping clear of the troubles that children bring down on their own heads.

'Master,' said one of his friends, 'do you say that we should obey *every* command of our parents, even if they tell us to do something that is wrong?'

The great man smiled. 'What do you think?' he asked, turning to a close friend. The man looked thoughtful but did not answer.

'Once upon a time,' said Confucius, 'there was a great king who ruled over many lands. He had so much power that he thought he could do anything he liked. He began to do the sort of wicked things that would surely have lost him his empire. Luckily he had seven wise ministers who warned him when he was about to do something wrong. He heeded their advice and kept his throne.

'Then there was a lord who owned a

castle and the land surrounding it as far as the eye could reach. As a young man he was as lazy as a crocodile. Money, he believed, was there to be spent and he threw it around him like a farmer's wife feeding her chickens. He would have lost all his riches if he had not had five friends who told him he was acting foolishly. He changed his ways and kept his lands.

'There was also a prime minister who ruled his country well. But he had some bad habits which, if they had become widely known, would have cost him his job. Worse, they would have lost the country a good ruler. It was just as well that he had three good servants who spoke up boldly and pointed this out to him. He gave up his wicked habits and continued to serve his country well.

'Now then,' said Confucius, 'each of these men was saved by people in a lower position. In the same way a father should be stopped if he orders his child to do something wicked. It is the right of every child to say no when told to do wrong; indeed, it is his duty. He should think so highly of his parents that he should be willing to risk their anger. He should say, "Look, I will not allow you to bring shame on yourselves by asking me to do this. I refuse."'

In those words Confucius gave the Chinese his rule: when you are told to do something wrong don't do it, no matter who orders you. Do you agree?

Solomon and the Baby

In the old days there was a king called Solomon. He was known as Solomon the Wise because of the sharpness of his mind and the fairness of his judgments. One day the captain of the guard led two young women into his court. 'Great king,' said one, 'I want you to decide between this woman and myself. We live in the same house, alone, and a short time ago each of us had a baby. One night this woman, turning over in her sleep, accidentally smothered her child. Naturally she was broken-hearted at the loss of her baby but listen to what she did.

'She stole over to the other bed where I was sleeping peacefully with my child. Gently she took my baby from my arms and put her dead one in its place. When I woke I knew the difference of course, but she insisted, and still insists, that the live baby is hers. I can't prove it's mine but it is.'

Then the other woman spoke. 'The baby is mine. What this woman says about the smothering of the other is true, but that was hers. She misses it so badly that she is prepared to steal mine.'

The two women fell silent, their eyes fixed pleadingly on Solomon. He thought for a few minutes and then said, 'We'll never be sure whose baby is still alive. My decision is that the infant be brought here, cut in two, and that one half of the body be given to each mother. That seems to

me the only fair solution. Don't you agree?'
His eyes searched the two women.

'Wise king,' said the woman who had spoken first, 'you are right as always. I'm willing to do as you say.'

'No no, please,' shouted the second woman. 'Don't kill the child. Let her have him. I give up my claim to him. Only don't kill him.'

The king smiled at her. 'You are the mother of the child,' he said. She was given the baby and happily left the palace. Later Solomon explained to some of his puzzled nobles, 'No real mother who cared about her baby could have him killed before her eyes. That's how I knew it was the second woman.'

The Royal Chatterbox

(Adapted from the Kacchapa Jataka)

The Buddhists tell us that their Jesus was born many times in different bodies – even those of animals. Once he was born to a noble family and grew up to become the king's chief minister. His Royal Highness had fine qualities but he had one maddening fault – he was a non-stop chatterbox. The prime minister – that is, the Buddha – knew it was his duty to warn his master that his tongue was making him look silly in the eyes of his people. However, he was nervous about how the king would take his advice and decided to wait for a suitable moment.

His chance soon came. Near the palace there was a lake in which a turtle lived. He was friendly with two wild geese who had come to spend the winter there. The three used to while away long hours chatting at the water's edge. Or rather, the geese used to spend long hours listening, for the turtle was a long-distance talker who loved the sound of his own voice. But the geese liked him so much that they were really sorry when the time came for them to return to their home in the north.

'I'd love to go with you,' said the turtle sadly.

'Why don't you?' said one of the geese.

'Oh, come on,' said the turtle, 'how could I get up there – fly?'

'Yes, in a way. Look, we'll take the

ends of a strong stick in our beaks. You hang on to the middle with your teeth. Then we'll take off and fly away. All you have to do is keep your mouth shut.'

The turtle thought this a fine idea and at once agreed. Next day the birds flew off, holding the stick in their beaks. Between them dangled the turtle, his teeth firmly gripping the stick. He was thrilled to find himself so far from earth, so near the clouds. Looking down, he saw the king's palace. It seemed no bigger than a birthday cake.

Just then a boy standing on a hill shouted, 'Blimey, look at the geese carrying the turtle. What a giggle!' The turtle, annoyed, could not stop himself from answering. He opened his mouth to roar an angry reply, and fell like a stone to the palace courtyard.

The king and the Buddha were among the first to gather round the shattered body. The Buddha seized his chance. With a deep sigh he said, 'What a pity! And what a grim lesson to those of us who cannot keep our mouths closed!'

His master looked at him with narrowed

eyes. 'I hope you're not referring to me,' he said coldly.

'I'm speaking of everyone,' said the Buddha. 'Your majesty, clever men like you and me know that people who talk too much never listen to others and so miss lots of chances of hearing new and worthwhile ideas. We also know that sooner or later they land themselves in a mess, like this unlucky turtle.'

The king looked thoughtful and mumbled something into his beard. From that moment he ceased to be a chatterbox.

Joseph and his Brothers

In the old days there was a man named Jacob who had twelve sons. By far his favourite was Joseph, the youngest but one, a boy who was said to be able to tell the future from dreams. To show his love for Joseph Jacob made a coat of many colours for him and the lad took great pleasure in wearing his gaily decorated garment, which stood out against the sober clothes of his brothers. Naturally they were jealous – a jealousy which grew as the years passed and their father showered more and more favours on Joseph.

One day, as they watched over their sheep, they made up their minds to get rid of him. They tossed him into a deep hole and would have left him to die if the eldest brother had not felt sorry for him at the last moment. He talked them into selling the boy to some travelling Egyptian tradesmen for twenty pieces of silver. Before letting him go they took his coat of many colours and dipped it in goat's blood. Then they waved goodbye to the Egyptians and their brother, ignoring his pitiful cries as he was pulled at the end of a rope towards a foreign country.

Back at home they showed Jacob the bloodstained coat. The poor father was shattered, for he was sure that his favourite son had been torn to pieces by a wild beast. He said he would grieve for his son for the rest of his life.

The brothers lived more pleasantly,

now that they had got rid of Joseph. They worked hard on the farm and turned it into a rich piece of land. They changed from sheep herding to crop farming and their barns were crammed every autumn with heavy golden corn.

Then one year the rains failed to come at the right time. Their harvest was a thin one but they comforted themselves with the thought that the next year would be better. It was not. The few straggly stalks were hardly worth gathering. Next year the drought continued and their land baked under a burning sun. The brothers and their ageing father were becoming desperate.

Seven years passed, each worse than the last. Their food stocks were gone. Then they heard that there was plenty of corn in Egypt. It appeared that the Egyptian prime minister had guessed that the famine was coming and had laid in huge supplies of corn. They decided to go and ask if they could buy some.

They travelled to Egypt as fast as they could and were lucky enough to be allowed to see the prime minister himself. As they bowed before him they were struck by the fact that he seemed a very young man to hold such an important post. They said they were willing to pay well for corn to fill their empty barns.

The prime minister looked at them strangely and asked many questions about their father and their youngest brother, Benjamin, whom they had left at home. Then he ordered the guards to take them to prison.

'He thinks we're spies,' whispered Reuben to his brothers in the darkness of their cells. Three days later they were freed, their sacks were filled with corn and they were told they could go home – all except Simeon. The prime minister said that he would keep Simeon until they brought back Benjamin, if they really had a brother called Benjamin. Off they went gratefully.

Old Jacob was delighted to see them come with the bulging sacks. Eagerly he slit open the precious bags. To everyone's amazement not only was each sack brimful, but the money they had paid was there too. Afraid that they might be accused of having stolen the money Jacob advised them not to go back to Egypt with the youngest brother. So they did not.

But soon their corn was used up and they were forced to return to Egypt with Benjamin. The prime minister freed Simeon, had their sacks filled with corn and sent them home. On their way to their father's house they were stopped by the prime minister's servants, who said that a valuable silver cup was missing. They demanded to search the brothers' sacks. When Benjamin's sack was opened the cup was discovered in it. The brothers were brought back in great fear to the prime minister. There they protested that Benjamin had not stolen the cup. The great man ordered all of them except Benjamin to go home. Benjamin, he said, would become his slave. Judah begged the prime minister to take him instead, saying that their father would be heartbroken at losing his youngest son.

Suddenly the prime minister burst into tears. 'I am your brother Joseph,' he said. 'I am the boy you sold into slavery. I was able to help the king of this country by telling him the meaning of his dreams and he made me his chief minister. I put the money in your sacks and the cup in Benjamin's to punish you. But I cannot keep up the pretence any longer. I forgive you for the wrong you did me and only want to see my father. Go, fetch him and come all of you and live here. I shall look after you.'

All the brothers embraced Joseph and wept to think of how wicked they had been. Then they set off for home. You can imagine the joy of Jacob to find that his long-lost son was alive. You can imagine his delight at meeting him again and living with him for the rest of his life.

When the Egyptians heard the full story they were struck with admiration for Joseph's actions. 'He has taught all of us,' they said, 'how to forgive those who do us wrong and how to help those who harm us.'

The Jars of Gold

(Adapted from a story by Sri Ramakrishna)

One day a barber was passing a haunted tree. Suddenly a strange voice said, ' How would you like to own seven jars of gold?'

The frightened man looked all around but could see no-one. ' It must be one of the good spirits that live in this tree,' he said to himself. He answered, ' I'd be delighted to have seven jars of gold.'

' Go home,' said the voice, ' and you'll find them there.'

Like a flash the excited man sped off towards his house. Sure enough, there stood seven large clay jars in the middle of his kitchen. A quick look told him that they were full of gleaming gold coins – all of them, that is, except one which was half-full. The barber laughed with joy, saying, ' I'm rich – richer than most kings. Now for a life of pleasure.' He began to plan the splendid palace he would build, the delicious meals, the wonderful clothes and all the other delights he would buy with his new-found riches.

Then his eye fell on the jar that was half-full. Why was it half-empty? he asked himself. Why had the good spirits filled six and not the seventh? It was a great pity, he thought, for half a jar of gold must be worth a lot of money. All at once his happiness seemed to have drained away. It was a dirty trick not to fill every jar.

Then he smiled. He knew what he'd do; he'd fill it himself. Yes, he wouldn't spend a penny of his wealth until he'd made that last jar as full as the others. Quickly he put all his valuable ornaments in a bag, sold them in the market, and dropped the gold coins he got for them into the jar. Then he took his savings, which he kept in a sock under the bed, and put them in too. He found that the extra gold did not seem to fill up the jar as much as he had hoped. He would have to find a lot more if he was to succeed, he told himself.

From then on he thought of nothing but filling the jar. He bought only the cheapest food. He spent next to nothing. Everything he saved was changed to gold and dropped in with the rest, but strangely enough it did not seem to raise the level of the coins. One day he went to the king, whose barber he was, and asked for a pay rise. His majesty looked puzzled at the skinny, ragged figure before him. Because he liked the man he agreed, although he thought he already paid him well.

Some weeks later the king was travelling in the royal coach when he saw the barber again. The miserable fellow was sitting at the roadside with a begging-bowl at his feet. When a passer-by came near he whined for a small coin.

The king stopped his coach and called him over. 'Look at you!' he said angrily. 'How on earth did you get into this state?' He stared in disgust at the ragged man's filthy clothes. The barber lowered his eyes in shame and could not speak. His majesty shook his head in a baffled way.

Suddenly a thought struck him. 'I say,' he said, 'I hope you haven't fallen for the old "seven jars" trick?'

'"S-s-seven jars" trick?' stammered the barber.

'Yes,' said the king, 'You know, the one where the bad spirit gives you seven jars, one of which is only half-full of gold, and you spend the rest of your life desperately trying to fill it.'

The barber nodded dumbly.

'Go back to the tree this minute,' ordered the king, 'and tell the evil spirit to take away the jars.' The poor man ran off and did as he was told. When he got home he found that the jars had gone, taking with them all the money he had scraped together. 'Never mind,' he said to himself. 'At least I've learned that greed only brings misery.'

The Good Samaritan

One day Jesus told a man with whom he was arguing that he ought to love his neighbour as much as he loved himself. 'Ah, yes,' said the man, 'but who is my neighbour? Is it the man next door or the lady in the next street or my cousin who lives across the sea? Who?'

Jesus answered, 'Perhaps this story will help you to decide. A man set out to walk to Jericho. On the way he was ambushed by some robbers who beat him up, robbed him and left him half-dead by the roadside. Soon a priest came along and saw the bloodstained figure on the ground. He hurried on past, for he didn't want to get mixed up in any unpleasantness.

'Next a Levite came along. You know who the Levites are; they are the tribe whose members look after the temple. Well, this Levite took a quick look at the injured man and headed on without lifting a finger to help.

'Then a Samaritan came down the road. Now you know what we Jews think of the Samaritans – that they're a rough, uneducated people, unlike ourselves. This Samaritan was on his knees in a flash bathing our friend's wounds and bandaging them. Then he gently picked him up and draped him over his donkey. Off he went for help. He came to an inn and said to the landlord, "I want this man well looked after. I have to go away now, but I'll be back. Take this money and use it to see that he has everything he needs. If there's any extra cost I'll pay it when I come back."

'Now,' said Jesus, 'which of the three men was a neighbour to the man who fell into the hands of the robbers?'

'The Samaritan,' was the reply.

'There's your answer,' said Jesus. 'Our neighbours are not just the people who live around us or our family or our friends. Our neighbours are those who reach out a hand when we need help. Now since even a Samaritan, whom we despise, will help a Jew, it follows that our neighbours are everybody.'

The Lady and the Guru

The old lady sat on a tuft of grass at the crossroads gazing along the dusty road. He should come about noon, she thought. At least that was what they had told her. She pulled her sari farther down over her face to lessen the glare of the burning Indian sun. Once again she picked up the plate and looked at the pies she had baked. There were two of them. Under their flaky brown pastry lay the best vegetables from the market. She thought of how she had worked to make these pies. Weary hours bent over her spinning-wheel had earned her enough money to buy the ingredients.

A crowd was beginning to gather at the roadside. Turbaned heads chattered and laughed. She heard a father explain, 'He's what we call a guru – a kind of holy teacher. We Sikhs listen to our gurus and do what they tell us. This one is called Har Rai. He's the seventh in a line that stretches back to Guru Nanak, the great founder of our faith. He's never been this way before, so . . .' At that moment a shout of 'Here he comes!' brought the old lady to her feet.

Sure enough, the great man had rounded the trees. He rode in a small party of horsemen dressed for hunting. They talked in low voices as their mounts picked their way towards the crossroads. The crowd raised a welcoming cheer. As the guru came abreast of her the old lady stepped for-

ward and held out the dish, too overcome to speak.

He reined in his horse. His friends followed suit. He gave the woman a long look. Then, smiling, he bent and took the pies. He ate them there and then, thanked her kindly, gave her much good advice and, with a wave of his hand, cantered off with the rest of his party.

His friends had watched all this with great surprise. Later they said to him, 'How could you do such a thing? You know very well that we Sikhs eat only food prepared by our own people in special ways. Those pies were made by a lower-caste person and were impure, unholy.'

'Nonsense,' said the guru, 'they were made holy by the hard work that went into preparing them. Holiness doesn't belong to the Sikhs, you know. It comes from inside. It's not all outward gestures and praying over food.'

Caesar's Coin

We are told that the priests and leading men among the Jews in Jerusalem became angry at Jesus for the repeated scoldings he gave them. They decided to trap him into saying something for which they could bring him to trial. One day several of them came to him and said, 'We admire your teachings and like the way you say what is in your mind no matter who likes or dislikes it. Now answer us this question. Should we pay taxes to the Romans or not?'

This was a very tricky question, for this reason. The Jews hated the Romans, who had taken over their land by force and made them pay money as taxes to the Roman emperor. Naturally the Jews bitterly disliked handing over money to their rulers. Now if Jesus answered that the Jews should not pay taxes to the Romans the priests intended to report this to the governor, who would take stern measures against him. If he said they should pay taxes the priests hoped to persuade the Jews that Jesus was a friend of the Romans and no true Jew.

Jesus saw through their plan. He said, 'Show me a silver coin.' Someone produced one. 'Whose head do you see on it?' he asked. 'Caesar the Roman emperor's,' was the reply.

'Very well then,' said Jesus, 'Seeing that it has his head on it you should pay it to him. Give to Caesar what belongs to Caesar and to God what belongs to God.'

His listeners knew exactly what he meant. Jesus was telling them that they should obey the laws of the land, which

meant paying taxes to the government, and that they should obey the laws of God, which involved leading a good private life. The reply was so well-judged that the enemies of Jesus knew that they could turn neither the Romans nor the Jews against him. So their attempt to catch him out failed.

The Blind Men and the Elephant

(Adapted from the Pali Canon)

Buddha, the Indian Jesus, said, 'Friends, long ago in this very city there lived a king who became weary of listening to the so-called wise men. You see, each of these men of learning had different ideas about the gods and the sacred books, and they used to argue with tongues like razors. One day the prince gathered together in the market place all the blind men in the city. Near them he placed an elephant. Then he told each man to go to the great beast and feel it with his hands. The first blind man advanced to the elephant and felt its head. The second took hold of its ear, the third its tusk, the fourth its trunk, the fifth its foot, the sixth its back, the seventh its tail and the last the tuft of the tail.

' " Now then," said the prince, " tell us what an elephant looks like."

' The first, who had felt his head, said, " It's like a pot."

' The next, the one who had touched the ear, said, " No, an elephant looks like a fan."

' " Nonsense! " laughed the man who had fingered the tusk, " it's round, hard and smooth like the handle of a plough."

' " Don't be daft," said the one who had felt the trunk. " The elephant is like a snake."

'To cut a long story short, each man described the animal differently. So the foot became a pillar, the back a barn, the tail a rope and the tuft a feather-duster. Each of the blind men was sure that he was right and all the others were wrong. At once a furious argument arose. Tempers rose and so did voices. Wild words were flung back and forth. One man punched another. There was a cry of pain. In a few moments the market place was a tangle of fighting bodies.

'The city's learned men looked on at all this, amazed and amused. The prince turned to them and said, "I don't know why you're laughing, gentlemen. Your own squabbles are just like these poor fellows'. You have your own narrow view of every question and you can't see anyone else's. You must learn to examine ideas all over, as the blind men should have examined the elephant. You'll never understand anything unless you look at it from many different angles." '

The Widow's Mite

One day Jesus was in the temple at Jerusalem. He was preaching to a crowd and arguing with them. Against the wall there was a large chest in which people were asked to put money to help with the upkeep of the temple, for it was a magnificent building and cost a lot to keep in good condition.

As he watched he saw many well-dressed men take gold and silver coins from their jewelled purses and toss them in the temple chest. Then along came an old lady, a widow, who fumbled in the pocket of her frayed cloak and took out two small coins. She dropped them in the chest and shuffled off.

'Did you see that?' said Jesus. 'Let me tell you this. That poor widow gave more than any of the rich men. After all, they had plenty of money left when they gave their gold and silver, but she has given everything she has.'

Jesus used this little happening to tell the people listening and us, that those who give as much as they can afford are as generous as much richer people who give more. He wanted to show that it is not the amount we give that is important but how great a sacrifice we have to make in order to give it.

POEMS

The Story of Bonnie and Clyde

By Bonnie Parker

You've heard the story of Jesse James –
Of how he lived and died.
If you're still in need
Of something to read,
Here's the story of Bonnie and Clyde.

Now Bonnie and Clyde are the Barrow
    Gang.
I'm sure you all have read

How they rob and steal
And those who squeal
Are usually found dying or dead.

They call them cold-hearted killers;
They say they are heartless and mean;
But I say this with pride,
That I once knew Clyde
When he was honest and upright and clean.

But the laws fooled around,
Kept taking him down
And locking him up in a cell,
Till he said to me,
I'll never be free,
So I'll meet a few of them in hell!

The road was so dimly lighted;
There were no highway signs to guide;
But they made up their minds,
If all roads were blind,
They wouldn't give up till they died.

The road gets dimmer and dimmer;
Sometimes you can hardly see;
But it's fight man to man,
And do all you can,
For they know they can never be free.

If they try to act like citizens,
And rent them a nice little flat,
About the third night
They're invited to fight.
By a submachine-gun rat-tat-tat.

They don't think they are too tough or
desperate,
They know the law always wins,
They have been shot at before
But they do not ignore
That death is the wages of sin.

From heartbreaks some people have
    suffered,
From weariness some people have died,
But take it all in all,
Our troubles are small,
Till we get like Bonnie and Clyde.

Some day they will go down together,
And they will bury them side by side.
To a few it means grief,
To the law it's relief,
But it's death to Bonnie and Clyde.

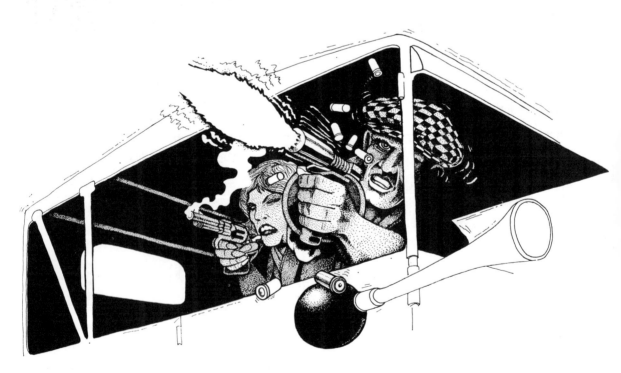

Abou Ben Adhem

by Leigh Hunt

Abou Ben Adhem (may his tribe increase!)
Awoke one night from a deep dream of
    peace,
And saw, within the moonlight in his room,
Making it rich, and like a lily in bloom,
An angel writing in a book of gold:
Exceeding peace had made Ben Adhem
    bold,
And to the presence in the room he said,
'What writest thou?' – The vision raised
    its head,
And with a look made all of sweet accord,
Answered, 'The names of those who love
    the Lord.'
'And is mine one?' said Abou. 'Nay, not
    so,'
Replied the angel. Abou spoke more low,
But cheerly still; and said, 'I pray thee
    then,
Write me as one that loves his fellow-men.'

The angel wrote, and vanished. The next
    night
It came again with a great wakening light,
And showed the names whom love of God
    had blessed,
And lo! Ben Adhem's name led all the
    rest.

The Tyger

By William Blake

Tyger! Tyger! burning bright
In the forests of the night,
What immortal hand or eye
Could frame thy fearful symmetry?

In what distant deeps or skies
Burnt the fires of thine eyes?
On what wings dare he aspire?
What the hand dare seize the fire?

And what shoulder, & what art,
Could twist the sinews of thy heart?
And when thy heart began to beat,
What dread hand? & what dread feet?

What the hammer? what the chain?
In what furnace was thy brain?
What the anvil? what dread grasp
Dare its deadly terrors clasp?

When the stars threw down their spears,
And water'd heaven with their tears,
Did he smile his work to see?
Did he who made the Lamb make thee?

Tyger! Tyger! burning bright
In the forests of the night,
What immortal hand or eye,
Dare frame thy fearful symmetry?

Jim Bludso of the Prairie Belle

by Colonel John Hay

Wall, no! I can't tell whar he lives,
   Becase he don't live, you see;
Leastways, he's got out of the habit
   Of livin' like you and me.
Whar have you been for the last three year
   That you haven't heard folks tell
How Jimmy Bludso passed in his checks
   The night of the Prairie Belle?

He weren't no saint, – them engineers
   Is all pretty much alike, –
One wife in Natchez-under-the-Hill
   And another one here, in Pike;
A keerless man in his talk was Jim,
   And an awkward hand in a row,
But he never flunked, and he never lied, –
   I reckon he never knowed how.

And this was all the religion he had, –
   To treat his engine well;
Never be passed on the river;
   To mind the pilot's bell;
And if ever the Prairie Belle took fire, –
   A thousand times he swore
He'd hold her nozzle agin the bank
   Till the last soul got ashore.

All boats has their day on the Mississip,
   And her day come at last, –
The Movastar was a better boat,
But the Belle she *wouldn't* be passed.
And so she come tearin' along that night –
   The oldest craft on the line –
With a nigger squat on her safety-valve,
   And her furnace crammed, rosin and
     pine.

The fire burst out as she clared the bar,
   And burnt a hole in the night,
And quick as a flash she turned, and made
   For that willer-bank on the right.
There was runnin' and cursin', but Jim
    yelled out,
   Over all the infernal roar,
' I'll hold her nozzle agin the bank
   Till the last galoot's ashore.'

Through the hot, black breath of the
    burnin' boat
   Jim Bludso's voice was heard,
And they all had trust in his cussedness,
   And knowed he would keep his word.
And, sure's you're born, they all got off
   Afore the smokestacks fell, –
And Bludso's ghost went up alone
   In the smoke of the Prairie Belle.

He weren't no saint, – but at jedgment
   I'd run my chance with Jim,
'Longside of some pious gentleman
   That wouldn't shake hands with him.
He seen his duty, a dead-sure thing, –
   And went for it thar and then;
And Christ ain't a-going to be too hard
   On a man that died for men.

Solitude

by Ella Wheeler Wilcox

Laugh, and the world laughs with you;
   Weep, and you weep alone;
For the sad old earth must borrow its mirth,
   But has trouble enough of its own.
Sing, and the hills will answer;
   Sigh, it is lost on the air;
The echoes bound to a joyful sound,
   But shrink from voicing care.

Rejoice, and men will seek you;
   Grieve, and they turn and go;
They want full measure of all your pleasure,
   But they do not need your woe.
Be glad, and your friends are many;
   Be sad, and you lose them all, –
There are none to decline your nectar'd
   wine,
   But alone you must drink life's gall.

Feast, and your halls are crowded;
   Fast, and the world goes by.
Succeed and give, and it helps you live,
   But no man can help you die.
There is room in the halls of pleasure
   For a large and lordly train,
But one by one we must all file on
   Through the narrow aisles of pain.

The Three Kings

by Henry W. Longfellow

Three Kings came riding from far away,
  Melchior and Gaspar and Baltasar;
Three Wise Men out of the East were they,
And they travelled by night and they slept
    by day,
    For their guide was a beautiful, wonder-
    ful star.

The star was so beautiful, large, and clear
  That all the other stars of the sky
Became a white mist in the atmosphere;
And by this they knew that the coming
    was near
  Of the Prince foretold in the prophecy.

Three caskets they bore on their saddle-
    bows,
Three caskets of gold with golden keys;
Their robes were of crimson silk with rows
Of bells and pomegranates and furbelows,
  Their turbans like blossoming almond
    trees.

And so the Three Kings rode into the West,
  Through the dusk of night over hill and
    dell,
And sometimes they nodded with beard on
    breast,
And sometimes talked, as they paused to
    rest,
  With the people they met at some way-
    side well.
'Of the Child that is born,' said Baltasar,
  'Good people, I pray you, tell us the
    news;

For we in the East have seen His star,
And have ridden fast, and have ridden far,
  To find and worship the King of the
    Jews.'

And the people answered: 'You ask in
    vain;
  We know of no King but Herod the
    Great!'
They thought the Wise Men were men
    insane
As they spurred their horses across the
    plain,
  Like riders in haste, and who cannot
    wait.

And when they came to Jerusalem,
  Herod the Great, who had heard this
    thing,
Sent for the Wise Men and questioned
    them;
And said: 'Go down unto Bethlehem,
  And bring me tidings of this new King.'

So they rode away; and the star stood still,
  The only one in the grey of morn;
Yes, it stopped, it stood still of its own free
    will,
Right over Bethlehem on the hill,
  The city of David, where Christ was
    born.

And the Three Kings rode through the
    gate and the guard,
  Through the silent street, till their horses
    turned
And neighed as they entered the great inn-
    yard;

But the windows were closed and the doors
    were barred,
  And only a light in the stable burned.

And cradled there in the scented hay,
  In the air made sweet by the breath of
    kine,
The little Child in the manger lay,
The Child that would be King one day
  Of a kingdom not human but divine.

His mother, Mary of Nazareth,
  Sat watching beside His place of rest,
Watching the even flow of His breath,
For the joy of life and the terror of death
  Were mingled together in her breast.

They laid their offerings at His feet;
  The gold was their tribute to a King,
The frankincense, with its odour sweet,
Was for the Priest, the Paraclete,
  The myrrh for the body's burying.

And the mother wondered and bowed her
    head,
  And sat as still as a statue of stone;
Her heart was troubled yet comforted,
Remembering what the angel had said
  Of an endless reign and of David's
    throne.

Then the Kings rode out of the city gate,
  With a clatter of hoofs in proud array;
But they went not back to Herod the Great,
For they knew his malice and feared his
    hate,
  And returned to their homes by another
    way.

Elegy on the Death of a Mad Dog

by Oliver Goldsmith

Good people all, of every sort,
  Give ear unto my song,
And if you find it wondrous short –
  It cannot hold you long.

In Islington there was a man,
  Of whom the world might say,
That still a godly race he ran –
  Whene'er he went to pray.

A kind and gentle heart he had,
  To comfort friends and foes;
The naked every day he clad –
  When he put on his clothes.

And in that town a dog was found,
  As many dogs there be,
Both mongrel, puppy, whelp, and hound,
  And curs of low degree.

This dog and man at first were friends,
  But when a pique began,
The dog, to gain some private ends,
  Went mad, and bit the man.

Around from all the neighbouring streets
  The wondering neighbours ran,
And swore the dog had lost his wits,
  To bite so good a man.

The wound it seem'd both sore and sad
  To every Christian eye;
And while they swore the dog was mad,
  They swore the man would die.

But soon a wonder came to light,
  That show'd the rogues they lied:
The man recover'd of the bite –
  The dog it was that died.

Matilda Who Told Lies and Was Burned to Death

by Hilaire Belloc

Matilda told such Dreadful Lies,
It made one Gasp and Stretch one's Eyes;
Her Aunt, who, from her Earliest Youth,
Had kept a Strict Regard for Truth,
Attempted to Believe Matilda:
The effort very nearly killed her,
And would have done so, had not She
Discovered this Infirmity.

For once, towards the Close of Day,
Matilda, growing tired of play,
And finding she was left alone,
Went tiptoe to the Telephone
And summoned the Immediate Aid

Of London's Noble Fire-Brigade.
Within an hour the Gallant Band
Were pouring in on every hand,
From Putney, Hackney Downs and Bow,
With Courage high and Hearts a-glow
They galloped, roaring through the Town,
'Matilda's House is Burning Down!'
Inspired by British Cheers and Loud
Proceeding from the Frenzied Crowd,
They ran their ladders through a score
Of windows on the Ball Room Floor;
And took Peculiar Pains to Souse
The Pictures up and down the House,
Until Matilda's Aunt succeeded
In showing them they were not needed
And even then she had to pay
To get the Men to go away!

. . . .

It happened that a few Weeks later
Her Aunt was off to the Theatre
To see that Interesting Play
The Second Mrs Tanqueray.
She had refused to take her Niece
To hear this Entertaining Piece:
A Deprivation Just and Wise
To Punish her for Telling Lies.
That Night a Fire *did* break out –
You should have heard Matilda Shout!
You should have heard her Scream and
    Bawl,
And throw the window up and call
To People passing in the Street –
(The rapidly increasing Heat
Encouraging her to obtain
Their Confidence) – but all in vain!
For every time She shouted 'Fire!'
They only answered 'Little Liar!'
And therefore when her Aunt returned,
Matilda, and the House, were Burned.

Harriet and the Matches

by Dr Heinrich Hoffman

It's really almost past belief
How little Harriet came to grief.
Mamma and Nurse went out one day
And left her all alone to play;
Now, on the table close at hand,
A box of matches chanced to stand;
And kind Mamma and Nurse had told her,
That, if she touched them, they should
    scold her.
But Harriet said: 'Oh, what a pity!
For, when they burn, it is *so* pretty;
They snap, and burn from red to blue;
All other people light them, too.'

The pussy-cats heard this,
And they began to hiss,
And stretch their claws
And raise their paws;
'Me-ow,' they said, 'me-ow, me-o!
You'll burn to death if you do so.'

But Harriet would not take advice,
She lit a match, it was so nice!
It crackled so, it burned so clear, –
Exactly like the picture here.
She jumped for joy and ran about
And was too pleased to put it out.

The pussy-cats saw this
And said: 'Oh, naughty, naughty Miss!'
And stretched their claws
And raised their paws :

' 'Tis very, very wrong, you know,
Me-ow, mee-o, me-ow, me-o!
You will be burnt, if you do so.'

And see! Oh! what a dreadful thing!
The fire has caught an apron-string;
Her apron burns, her arms, her hair;
She burns all over, everywhere.
Then how the pussy-cats did mew,
What else, poor pussies, could they do?
They screamed for help, 'twas all in vain!
So then they said: ' We'll scream again;
Make haste, make haste, me-ow, me-o.
She'll burn to death, we told her so.'

So she was burnt, with all her clothes,
And arms, and hands, and eyes and nose;
Till she had nothing more to lose
Except her little scarlet shoes. . . .
And nothing else but these was found
Among her ashes on the ground.

FICTION

The Coffee-house at Surat

(After Bernardin de Saint-Pierre)

A number of men from different countries were chatting in an Indian café. The conversation came around to God. An African slave took a small wooden idol from his pocket and said that that was his god. He was at once scolded by an Indian who said that Brahma, his god, was the only true one. A Jew in turn contradicted the Indian, saying that the real god was the god of his people, the god of Abraham, Isaac and Jacob. Next an Italian priest declared that the true god was only to be found in the Catholic Church of Rome. A Protestant minister said that God helped anyone who believed in Him and lived a good life. A Turk said that nobody believed in the Christian god any more; Allah, worshipped by the Mohammedans, was the real god.

The argument grew hot and heavy as first one man and then another spoke up and lectured the others. Each was sure that he knew the truth of the matter and all the rest were talking nonsense. Then they all noticed that a Chinaman who was sitting with them had not opened his mouth.

'You've been very quiet,' said one to him. 'Now tell us your opinion.'

The Chinaman removed the pipe from

his mouth. 'Let me answer by telling a story,' he said. 'Once there was a group of men sitting on the sand talking about the sun, which at the moment was pouring its warm rays on them. A blind man said, "There is no such thing as the sun. I have never seen it, so for me it simply doesn't exist."

' "No, my friend," said another, a lame man who hobbled about the fishing village on crutches, "you are wrong, for I see the sun every day. It is a great ball of fire which rises out of the sea every morning and goes to sleep among the mountains."

' "Nonsense!" exclaimed a fisherman. "If you went out to sea as I do you would know the sun rises and sets in the sea."

'An Indian laughed. "How could the sun be a ball of fire?" he asked. "If it were it would be put out by the water. No, the sun is the god Deva who during the day rides across the heavens in a chariot. At night he is attacked and swallowed by two great snakes. Then our priests pray, and the snakes open their mouths and let the sun go free. So we have a new day."

' "Wrong!" said an Egyptian. "I'm a sailor and I've travelled all over the world. The truth is that the sun lights the whole earth and goes down in the sea far, far in the west, beyond England."

'An English sailor spoke up. "Gentlemen, I can put all your minds at rest. I too have been all over and I tell you that I have seen the sun appear to rise and set in every imaginable place. Actually it rises and sets nowhere. The sun travels round and round the earth, just as the moon travels around the earth."

'Up spoke a ship's pilot. "You are all wrong," he said gently. "It was proved long ago that the earth moves around the sun. Because the earth spins round on itself once a day it turns away from the sun, giving the appearance of sunrise and sunset. That is the truth."'

The Chinaman looked from face to face of his silent listeners. 'Do you see why I told you that story?' he asked. 'Just as each of those men saw the sun as it affected his own life so each of you wants to have a special god of his own, or at least a special god for his own group. But the real god is like the sun as the ship's pilot described it. He is for everyone, and we revolve around Him, not He around us.'

The Soldier, the Scientist and the Sausages

Many years ago the leader of a far country was a rough, soldierly man. In fact he had spent much of his time as a young man at the wars. He greatly admired strength of body and strength of mind. He believed that if you wanted something the thing to do was go out and get it. If someone got in your way you stepped on him. He looked down on anyone who was too mild to fight. Life, he would say, was a fight and the real prizes in life could not be won without a struggle. In every struggle someone was bound to get hurt, so there was no use in wasting sympathy on those who were too weak to fight.

But since he was also a clever man and because he fought so well for his country, his people admired him. They gave him important posts in their government, and at last he became their leader. This did not change his nature. He continued to believe that violence was the way to get what you wanted. He seemed to prove this by making war on one of his neighbour countries and winning easily. His people looked up to him even more.

It happened that he was at a party one night. There were many guests in a large room, laughing, drinking, moving about, chatting. Suddenly everyone was startled to hear their leader shout, 'Sir, you have insulted me. I challenge you to a duel.' He was red-faced and trembling with rage. The man he had shouted at was a quiet-looking little person who looked as if butter wouldn't melt in his mouth.

Now duelling was fairly common in those days. If a man felt he had been insulted he might choose to settle the matter by a fight with swords or pistols. It was against the law and sensible people, especially those who had no skill with weapons, refused to fight.

The party-goers fully expected the little man to turn down the duel. After all, someone whispered, he was a professor of chemistry at the university and it was hardly fair to challenge him. To their surprise the professor agreed to fight.

'Good,' said the soldier. 'I shall call for you first thing tomorrow morning.'

At dawn there was a knock at the professor's door and the soldier stalked in. 'Are you ready?' he asked.

'Yes,' was the calm reply.

'Have you chosen your weapons?'

'Yes,' said the professor.

'Where are they?' asked the soldier, who could see no weapons.

'There they are,' said the professor, pointing to a plate on which lay two sausages.

'I've no time for joking,' said the soldier. 'Choose your weapons and let's get on with it.'

'I'm not joking,' said the scientist. 'Those are my weapons. Let me explain.

This morning I fried the sausages. Then I took a syringe – a sort of hollow needle – and squirted into one of them a deadly

poison, so powerful that whoever eats that sausage will die within a few minutes in dreadful pain. Both sausages should taste excellent and indeed the good one is excellent. Now my idea is that you choose one of them and I'll take the other. One of us will enjoy a well-cooked sausage, while the other . . .' The professor shook his head sadly.

The soldier looked amazed. ' I've never heard anything like it,' he said. ' Look here, this is not the way a brave man fights. He fights with swords or pistols. Those are the weapons of men.'

' Nonsense,' said the professor. ' Swords and pistols are the weapons of little boys. Really grown-up people know that fighting is for those who remain children all their lives. You speak of bravery but the only kind you know is swaggering and shooting and killing. You know nothing about the bravery of, say, a poor widow bringing up her family on a few shillings a week. *You* wouldn't call a doctor brave who went into the slums to treat his patients in the middle of a plague. There are a million acts of courage carried out by ordinary people every day. Your kind of bravery is fit only for bullies like yourself.

' But I'm getting away from the point. You have challenged me to a duel. I have chosen my weapons. Pick up your weapon, if you have the nerve, and eat it. I will follow suit. I'm waiting.'

The soldier stood for a long time looking down at the sausages. Once or twice his hands twitched as if he was on the brink of choosing. Then he slowly shook his head and said, ' No.'

The Gift of the Magi

(Adapted from the story by O. Henry)

It was Christmas Eve in the morning many years ago. A young man and his wife sat at the breakfast table.

' What a miserable Christmas we're going to have,' said the young man. ' I haven't even enough money to buy you a present.'

' Nor I you, Jim,' said his wife. ' Still, let's suppose you had some money. What would you buy me?'

' That's easy,' said her husband. ' I've been looking at some of the women's magazines and I see that these tortoiseshell combs are all the rage – you know, the sort women use to sweep their hair up and keep it in position. Your long red hair would look splendid swept up on the top of your head.' His wife laughed with pleasure.

' But what about me?' continued Jim. ' If you had some money what would you buy me?'

' Simple,' said the young wife, ' I'd buy you a platinum chain for your pocket watch. I know you don't like the old leather strap you use. It's easy to see how proud you are of that watch – I've seen the way you take it out of your waistcoat pocket and nurse it in the palm of your hand – and I know you'd love to have a platinum chain stretching from one pocket to the other, like other men.'

' Quite correct, Della,' said her hus-

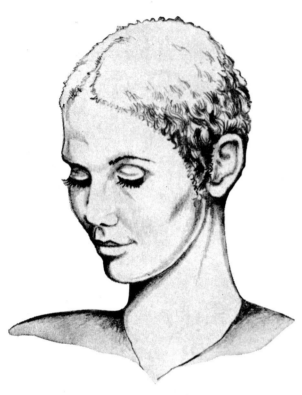

think she bought? Yes, a platinum chain. On her way home she smiled as she thought of the delight Jim would feel when he first handled the glittering thing.

Back at home again another, not so pleasant, thought struck her. 'Oh, dear,' she said to herself, 'he'll be sad that I've had all my hair cut off. He did admire it so much. I'll have a go at it with the curling tongs. I'm sure I can pretty it up a bit.' She did just that and managed to make herself look like a curly-headed boy.

When Jim came home from work he stared dumbfounded at the change in Della's appearance.

'Now don't be annoyed,' she said. 'It'll grow again in no time. I was well paid for it and I've got you a Christmas present.' From behind her back she brought the gaily packaged box. He took it, unwrapped it slowly and gazed with a strange expression at the gleaming chain. He seemed too surprised to speak.

'Come on,' said Della, 'let's fit it on your watch.' She put her hand in his waistcoat pocket. It was not there. She tried the other pocket. It was not there either.

'Where is it?' she asked in surprise.

'I sold it,' came the answer.

'Why?' she asked with an astonished expression.

'To buy you a present,' he said, pulling an ornamental box from his pocket.

She took the box and opened it. Guess what it contained. Yes, the set of tortoiseshell combs.

'Do you see what we've done?' said the husband. 'You sold your hair to buy a chain for my watch, which I sold to buy

band, taking out his old gold watch, worn smooth by the hands of his father and grandfather.

'Goodness,' he said, 'I'm late. I must fly.' He quickly kissed his wife and left for work.

When he had gone Della stared miserably at herself in the mirror. How could she buy Jim a present? Suddenly a brilliant idea struck her and her face lit up in a smile. Quickly she grabbed her hat and coat and went out.

Half an hour later Della came out of a wigmaker's shop. Her long hair was gone, replaced by a short stubble which looked like a badly-mown lawn. She had sold her hair to Madame Sofronie for a good sum, enough to get that precious present. She hurried to the jeweller's and what do you

combs for your hair, which you sold . . .' He stopped and they stared at each other. Then both began to laugh at the strange thing that had happened to them. They laughed till the tears rolled down their cheeks although, come to think of it, there was not all that much to laugh at. He had lost his precious watch and she had lost her beautiful hair.

But that was the happiest Christmas they ever had. Although they had not much in the way of rich food and drink, they knew that each had given up something very dear to make the other happy.

The Last Leaf

(Adapted from a story by O. Henry)

Two young women named Sue and Johnsy shared a flat in New York. They hoped to become artists some day, but for the present they earned their living by doing advertising posters and magazine pictures.

One autumn Johnsy fell ill and took to her bed. She quickly got worse and Sue, very alarmed, sent for the doctor.

'Pneumonia,' he said to Sue outside the bedroom. 'I'm afraid she has very little chance. You see, she doesn't seem to want to live. Sick people must fight to get better. She won't. She's just lying there waiting for the end.'

When Sue went back into the bedroom she found Johnsy lying still, her pale face turned towards the window.

'Twelve,' whispered Johnsy, and then, 'eleven.'

'What on earth are you saying?' asked Sue.

'I'm counting. When the last leaf falls I shall go too.'

Sue looked out of the window across the narrow yard. On the wall opposite she saw an old ivy vine, its withered leaves fluttering in the bitter wind. As she watched another leaf fell to the ground.

'Ten,' said Johnsy in a feeble voice. 'I'll watch the ivy dying as I'm dying, and when the last leaf dies so will I.'

'I never heard such nonsense,' said Sue firmly, but she was desperately worried, for she could see that the doctor had been right when he said that Johnsy did not want to live.

Later that day Sue told old Mr Behrman about it all. He was a poor painter who lived downstairs. He kept saying that some day he would paint a masterpiece, but no-one believed him any longer. He was saddened by the news of his young friend. Grimly he looked at the ivy. The wind was rising and the dark clouds threatened rain. Darkness was falling. Six leaves bravely clung to the wall. Would they last until morning, the old man asked himself?

Next morning Johnsy's first weak words to Sue were, 'Pull back the curtains. Let me see the tree.' With hands that trembled Sue slid the pink curtains apart. One leaf stood out against the brick wall. Sue gasped with relief. Johnsy stared in surprise and then whispered, 'When that one falls I'll go too.'

The day wore on and even through the twilight they could see the lone ivy leaf outlined against the wall. As night fell Sue was frightened to hear the north wind rising again. She prayed that the last leaf would cling to the tree, for she knew that Johnsy meant to die when it fell.

When it was light enough next morning Johnsy asked Sue to draw the curtains. The frightened girl rose and, with a prayer on her lips, drew them back. The leaf was still there. Johnsy looked at it for a long time in a very puzzled way. Then she said, 'Sue, something has made that leaf stay there to show me how wrong it is to want to die. So I'm not going to. Do you think I might have a little soup?'

Joyfully Sue prepared the soup. She now knew that the danger was past. Her friend had got back her desire to live, and that was more than half the battle.

A few days later Johnsy was sitting up in bed knitting. 'Isn't that leaf remarkable?' she said. 'Look, it hasn't fallen yet, and the winds have been screaming around it for the last two nights.'

Sue said gently, 'There's something I'm sorry to have to tell you. Old Mr Behrman died in hospital today. They found him collapsed in his room the other morning, fully clothed and blue with cold. They were puzzled by the fact that he had a torch in one hand and his painting palette in the other. Yesterday I solved the problem. He must have seen that all the leaves had blown down, so during the night he took a ladder, climbed up the wall and painted a leaf on the bricks. That's why it didn't fall – will never fall. You could say it was his masterpiece, and he did it to save your life.'

King Charles Sets a Problem

King Charles II was known as the Merry Monarch, for he was a cheerful man who believed that life was there to be enjoyed. He saw no reason why a king should not lead as happy a life as any ordinary person, so he amused himself like anyone else without worrying too much about his kingly dignity.

There was, however, another side to his character. He was deeply interested in science. In his own workshop he conducted experiments on floating objects. He encouraged scientists in many ways. Often he was present at meetings of the Royal Society, a body of thinkers who had set out to find out more about the workings of nature.

A story is told – no-one knows whether it is true or not – that one day during a meeting of the scientists King Charles said to them, 'Gentlemen, I'd be grateful if you could answer this question for me; if you weigh a basin of water and then weigh it again with a live fish in it the weight stays the same. But if you weigh a basin of water and then weigh it again with a dead fish in it the weight goes up by the weight of the dead fish. Why is that? Please give me an answer when we next meet.'

The great brains met to solve this strange puzzle. Although all the cleverest men in the land were there nobody seemed to have the answer. Why, they asked each other, should a live fish weigh nothing and

a dead fish something? Some came up with reasons which were easily proved wrong by others. Many searched through great piles of books, but without success. It looked as if all the finest minds in England would have to admit defeat and tell the king that they could not answer his question.

Then one man said timidly, 'Perhaps there is no difference in weight between a live and a dead fish. It might be an idea to fetch a basin of water and see if it's really true.'

The other scientists were shocked. After all, the king had said that it was so, therefore it must be so. To contradict this meant saying that the king himself was wrong. This was almost treason, they told the poor fellow, and many a man in days gone by had had his head chopped off for less.

They carried on with their hopeless attempts to solve the king's puzzle. Idea after idea was put forward and thrown out, but they seemed no nearer an answer. Then the awkward fellow meekly asked if they would carry out a little experiment to see if the dead fish weighed more. To keep him quiet they agreed.

He fetched a basin of water and weighed it on the scales. Then he put in a live fish. To everyone's surprise the pan holding the basin went down, showing that the fish must weigh something. Then he took out the fish and left it to die. Next he put the dead fish into the basin. It weighed exactly the same as it had when it was alive.

The scientists now knew that the king had played a trick on them. But some thought he had a more serious purpose. The king, they said, was teaching the thinkers that they must not believe something just because a king says so. He was saying that we must not accept an idea blindly just because an important person says it is true.

Much Ado About Practically Nothing

Just as the train was about to pull out of the station a young man came dashing on to the platform, swung open a carriage door, jumped in and thankfully banged the door behind him. He walked along the corridor until he came to an empty carriage. Entering, he slid the door shut after him, sat down heavily and put his feet up on the opposite seat.

This is a bit of all right, he thought to himself. I've got a carriage to myself. I hate sharing with other people. They do chatter and eat and disturb me. I'm glad I shut the door behind me. That should keep everybody out.

At that very moment the door was slid open and a middle-aged woman entered, carrying a tiny poodle. She stopped and looked coldly down at the young man's outstretched legs. Slowly, unwillingly, the man took his feet off the seat and put them on the floor. Without a word of thanks she passed him and sat beside the window, seating the poodle on her lap.

The train moved off. The two people sat in silence, she staring out of the window, the young man glancing idly around the carriage. Then she rose and let down the window half-way. At once an icy blast of air came swirling into the carriage. The man shivered, drew his thin raincoat closer round his neck and said, 'Excuse me, but do you mind if we have that window up again? It is a very cold December day and I'm quite frozen in this draught.'

She looked at him without expression. 'I'm quite warm,' she said, and continued looking at the passing countryside.

'Don't you think you're being rather selfish?' asked the young man. 'After all, you didn't ask me whether I wanted the window open.'

To this there was no reply. He glared at her but she behaved as if he had not spoken – indeed, as if he wasn't there. Then he had an idea. He took out his pipe and lit up. Within seconds he was puffing great clouds of smoke into the air. Soon the rich smell of strong tobacco filled the carriage.

'Young man,' said the woman coldly, 'would you be so good as to put out that pipe? It's the height of rudeness to smoke a filthy thing like that in an enclosed space in the presence of a stranger. Will you please put it out?'

'No,' said he, and he carried on puffing with every sign of enjoyment. She gave him a long, angry stare which did not make the slightest difference to his behaviour. He continued smoking as if he was in his favourite armchair at home. Then a slight smile crossed her lips. She let the poodle slip from her lap on to the floor.

The little fellow's first action was to sniff at the man's shoe. Then he licked it. The young man frowned in annoyance and crossed his legs, taking the shoe away from the dog's nose. It began to sniff the other shoe. Then it took the lace between its teeth and tugged. The lace came undone.

'Will you please keep your dog – if that's what it is – under control?' asked the man.

'No,' she answered in exactly the tone he had used to her. 'And may I say that you're the rudest person I've met for many a long day.'

He replied, 'Which leaves me free to tell you that you're the most self-centred person I've ever had the misfortune to share a railway carriage with.'

She flushed with rage, grabbed the pipe from his mouth and threw it out of the window. Quick as a flash he picked up the poodle and threw it out after the pipe.

Then they sat and glared speechlessly at each other.

After a little while, when her anger had died down somewhat, she began to think that perhaps she had not behaved very well. Looking back on what had happened she saw that she was to blame for at least part of the foolish row. She wished she had not acted as she had. She decided to tell the young man she was sorry for what she had done.

While she was thinking how best she could apologize he spoke. 'Look,' he said, 'I'm sorry for what I've done. My behaviour has been disgraceful. Filling the carriage with smoke was bad enough but throwing your dog out was shameful. As for calling you selfish, well, I'm afraid I'm the selfish one. You see, I hoped to have the place to myself and your entry annoyed me in the first place.'

'I was about to tell you that I was sorry for my actions,' said the woman. 'My behaviour over the window and the dog and the pipe is something that I'd like to forget. Please forgive me for scolding you for rudeness. I know now who was the more rude of the two of us.'

The young man smiled and they continued their journey on the best of terms, chatting and enjoying each other's company.

When they reached their destination they stayed talking on the platform for a little while. Suddenly, guess what came running up to them along the platform. Yes, that's right, the poodle. And you'll never guess what he had in his mouth. Yes, you've got it – his tongue.

Antigone

(Adapted from the play by Sophocles)

In olden times a young man named Polynices raised an army and marched to attack the city in which he had been born and brought up. The king, who was his uncle, sent out an army to defend the city. This army was led by the brother of Polynices.

There was a battle. The city's army won, but the two brothers died, each killed by the other. The king, whose name was Creon, had his dead general's body brought back to the city and buried with great honour. He ordered that the corpse of the traitor Polynices should be left on the battlefield to be eaten by dogs and vultures. Anyone who buried the body, said Creon, would be put to death.

Antigone, the sister of the dead man, went out and buried the body. The king's soldiers found the burial place and dug up the corpse, leaving it once again where it had fallen. The girl was brought before Creon who said sternly, 'You have broken the city's laws. The fact that you are my niece and engaged to 'be married to my son Haemon will not save you. The law is the same for everyone.'

'I am quite willing to die,' said the girl. 'I would rather be killed than live on and let my brother's body lie unburied on the battlefield.'

'So you honoured the body of a traitor as much as we honoured that of his brother who died defending his city. And to do it you broke the law. Don't you know that without law we should be wild animals?'

Antigone said proudly, 'I am sure that neither of my brothers would blame me for burying the other's body. As for breaking the law, I am proud to have done it. There are some laws which are higher than human ones, and the duty of honouring our dead comes before any rules you dream up.'

Creon saw that argument was useless and ordered his niece to be taken to the cells to prepare for her death. His son Haemon entered. He told his father that it was wrong to put Antigone to death. The people of the city felt she had done right, he said. He pleaded with Creon to spare the girl, if only for the king's own sake. Creon answered that a king must make the laws and see that they are kept. He knew that Haemon loved Antigone and dearly wished to marry her, but a king must place the city's laws above the happiness of anyone, even his own son. Haemon left in anger, saying that he would never see his father again.

Next came Teiresias, the wisest man in the city, who told the king that enough blood had been spilled and that he should forgive Antigone. Creon refused point-blank. Teiresias warned him that he would suffer for the girl's death. The killing, he said sadly, would not end with her. Then the old man left.

Creon at once ordered the guard to take Antigone to an underground cave and leave her to die. When the order had been carried out the king thought over what he had done. He knew he had acted only for the good of the city. It was a great pity that his own niece, who was to marry his son, should have to die, but she had known the penalty and must pay the price. Then he remembered the words of Haemon and Teiresias. Each had pleaded for the girl's life. Haemon had warned him that the people were on Antigone's side. Teiresias had spoken of more deaths to follow.

For the first time Creon wondered if he had done right. Perhaps Teiresias had spoken the truth; there had been enough killing. Was Antigone right when she said that her first duty was to bury her brother, whatever the law laid down? The more Creon pondered the more he came to believe that he had been wrong. I must act at once, he thought, to undo the harm I've done before it is too late.

The king rose. Gathering his soldiers he went to the battlefield and buried Polynices's body. Then he hurried to the cave to free Antigone. There he found his son Haemon holding in his arms the dead body of the girl. She had hanged herself rather than wait for a slow death. Creon moved towards his son to comfort him but the boy spat at him and drew his sword. Overcome with sorrow and shame Creon left with his soldiers. Haemon rested the hilt of his sword on the rocky ground, placed the point at his breast and fell on the blade. He died almost at once.

When Creon's wife heard of the death of her son she, too, killed herself. Creon wished that he also was dead. He knew that by his stubborn insistence that the laws must be obeyed he had caused the death of his wife and son. Antigone had been right when she said that people were more important than rules.

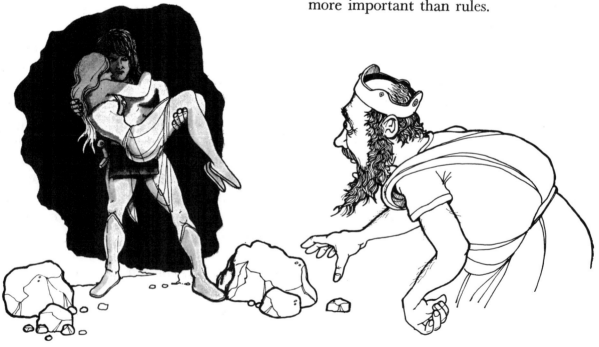

Leonardo and 'The Last Supper'.

I must confess that the story I'm going to tell isn't true. It can't be true, the experts say. Yet it's such a strange tale and has such a good idea behind it that it's worth listening to.

Hundreds of years ago the monks in a big monastery in Italy decided that they would like a large painting of the last supper of Jesus on the wall of their dining-hall. They asked Leonardo da Vinci, who was thought to be the best painter in Italy, to do it for them. He set to work and in time produced a picture which became widely admired. You may have seen photographs of it in books. It shows the twelve apostles of Jesus seated along one side of a long table. In the middle, his head framed by an open window, sits the figure of Jesus.

The story goes that the painter decided to paint Jesus first. He thought it best to paint from a model, that is, to get someone to represent Jesus while he painted. Now he wanted to show Jesus as the kindest, noblest-looking man ever seen. He took to walking the streets peering at men's faces, searching for the one he needed. It took some time, for he was very hard to please, but at last he found what he wanted. He met a young man whose face seemed to glow with the majesty he wished to show. He hurried up to him, explained what he wanted and asked the young man to sit and be painted by him. He agreed and came several times to the monastery where Leonardo skilfully got that fine head into his picture. Then one day the painter paid him a small fee, thanked him for his trouble and bade him goodbye.

Leonardo next painted the apostles of Jesus. He took just as much trouble with their portraits, seeking out a live model every time he started a new face. Often he did not go near the painting for days and some of the monks began to complain that he would never finish it. In addition, he spent much time experimenting with new paints and varnishes. He lost more time by taking on work for other people, for he was not only a painter but an engineer, architect and sculptor.

Years passed. The painting had slowly come near to completion. There was one more thing to do – the figure of Judas, the man who betrayed Jesus. Leonardo decided that Judas must have a face in which greed and treachery stood out – a face stamped with wickedness. With his usual care he set out to find a man who looked like his idea of Judas.

He first went to the prisons and studied all the worst criminals there. None looked wicked enough. Next he sought out all the well-known villains who were not for the moment behind bars. Most of them looked like saints. Finally he toured all the drinking places and gambling dens, beginning to feel that he would never find what he wanted. Then he found him.

He was crouched over a bottle in a filthy cellar. Leonardo thought he had never seen such an evil expression on a human face. He approached the man and told him he wished to paint him and would pay a small fee. The man agreed at once.

Back at the monastery Leonardo seated his model in a chair and got busy with his painting. He had done only a few brush-strokes when, glancing over his shoulder to study the man's face, he saw to his astonishment great tears rolling down his cheeks.

'What's the matter?' asked the painter.

'Years ago,' said the man, 'when you began this painting you looked for a model for Jesus and you chose – me. Since then I've lived a life of wickedness and now I look like your idea of Judas. That's why I'm crying.'

The Bishop's Candlesticks

(Adapted from *Les Miserables* by Victor Hugo)

The story of the bishop's candlesticks is not really true but it is worth telling. It happened one night when the bishop was about to sit down to have his supper. The door opened and a big, rough-looking man appeared. His name, he said, was Jean Valjean and he had just been freed after nineteen years as a galley-slave. A galley-slave was a criminal who served his time chained to an oar, rowing the old wooden ships.

The bishop calmly invited the man to sit down and have supper with him. His housekeeper laid the table for three, for the bishop's sister lived with him. She set out the silver knives and forks and placed two handsome candlesticks on the table. These were the last of the bishop's treasures, for he had given away all his other possessions to the poor.

Jean Valjean ate like a wolf. He had been turned away from many doors that night and was very hungry. When he had finished he asked if the bishop had a stable where he could bed down for the night. The bishop said that he could sleep in the spare room. He picked up one of the silver candlesticks and led the ex-convict to the bedroom by the light of the flickering flame.

In the middle of the night Valjean

Quickly he unlocked it and took out the box of silverware. A minute later he was outside the house beneath the stars. He emptied the silver into his bag, threw away the box, climbed the wall and was gone.

Next morning the housekeeper came running to tell the bishop that the silver had vanished with Valjean. He listened quietly and then said, 'The man was poor and needed the silver. From now on we'll use ordinary knives and forks.'

At that moment there was a knock at the door and three policemen entered holding Jean Valjean. The bishop rose and walked towards the thief. 'I'm glad to see you,' he said, 'but you forgot to take the candlesticks as well as the rest of the silverware I gave you.'

Valjean stared in complete astonishment.

The police sergeant spoke. 'So this fellow's story is true!' he said in great surprise. 'We thought it strange to find a rascally-looking person like this with a bag of fine silver, but he told us that you had given it to him.'

'Quite right,' said the bishop. 'My friend, before you go, here are your candlesticks. Take them.' He held them out to the dumbfounded thief who took them with hands that trembled. The bishop said in a low voice, 'Jean Valjean, you no longer belong to evil, but to good.'

From that day on the galley-slave was a different man. The bishop's kindness had changed him. He finished his life as fine and generous a man as the old priest who had saved him from going back to the galleys.

awoke. He rose. Silently he stole through the sleeping household. He made for the cupboard in which he had seen the housekeeper put away the knives and spoons.

The Repentant Sinner

(Adapted from a story by Tolstoy)

An old man lay dying. As he waited for death he looked back over his life. It was a story of wickedness, for he had made up his mind when a young man to get everything he wanted in whatever way he could. He trembled as he thought of the judgment which his mother had taught him comes to all of us after we have left this world. Soon his eyes closed, his mind darkened and he died.

He woke up outside the door of Heaven. He banged on the smooth wood and shouted, 'Let me in.'

'Who is this man and how did he live on earth?' asked an angry voice from inside. Another, deeper voice answered, giving the old man's name and starting on a recital of his crimes. As the list rolled on, detailing every one of his villainies, the old man covered his face in shame. How could he ever hope to get into Heaven after such a wicked life? When the accusing voice stopped the other voice said, 'I'm sorry, we couldn't possibly let a rascal like you into Heaven.'

'Who's that speaking?' asked the old man.

'I am Peter,' came the answer, 'the friend of Jesus who became the leader of his followers after his death.'

The old man said desperately, 'Well then, you must know something of human weakness. Didn't you fall asleep when Jesus asked you to stay awake with him the night before he was killed? And didn't you say three times that you didn't even know him because you were afraid they would put you to death?'

There was a long silence from inside the door. Then came the sound of footsteps walking away. The old man began once again to batter on the wood. After a little while a new voice said, 'Who's that?'

'Please let me in,' said the old man.

'Who is this man and how did he live on earth?' asked the new voice. The deep tones answered with the man's name and a list of his sins.

'I'm sorry,' said the new voice, 'but we couldn't have a villain like you up here.'

'Who's that speaking?' asked the old sinner.

'I am King David,' was the reply.

'But you too have shared some of my wickednesses,' said the old man. 'Didn't you put Uriah at the front of the battle so that he would be killed and you could take his widow Bathsheba?'

There was a long silence and then the sound of quick footsteps scurrying away. The old rascal banged away once more on the great oak door. At last a fresh voice said, 'What do you want?'

'I want to go in.'

'Who is this man and how did he live on earth?'

Once again came the long and damning list of crimes.

'We can't let anyone like that in here,' said a shocked voice.

'Who's that speaking?' asked the old

man, by now sure that he had no chance of being allowed in.

'I am John, sometimes called John the Divine, who wrote down the story of Jesus.'

'I'm glad to hear it,' said the sinner, 'for wasn't it you who wrote that God is love? Didn't you write that Jesus said he was the good shepherd? Don't you think that your good shepherd would welcome back a lost sheep who has strayed from the flock?'

There was a long silence. Then the great door swung open and John stood there smiling.

'Come in,' he said.

Little Girls Wiser Than Men

(Adapted from a story by Tolstoy)

When Malasha came out into the village street she found that the snow had melted and formed a pool in the middle of the road. She walked out to its edge and saw that it was deep enough to paddle in. At that moment Akulya came along. The two girls looked around to see if anyone was watching. There was no-one. Then they took off their shoes and stockings and paddled in the water. At first it was so cold that they squealed with shock and pleasure.

'Be careful not to splash me,' said Akulya. 'This is a new dress and my mother'll skin me if I get it dirty.'

Malasha playfully kicked up the water with her foot, never dreaming that it could reach the other girl. But it did. Up rose a small fountain of dirty water and left a trail of splashes all the way down the front of Akulya's new white dress.

'Look what you've done,' shouted Akulya, bursting into tears.

'I'm sorry. I honestly didn't mean it,' said Malasha, appalled at what she had done.

A fierce argument broke out between the two girls. Voices were raised and some hard words were used. Suddenly Akulya's mother came on the scene. When she saw the state of her daughter's dress and heard that Malasha had done it she lifted her hand and smacked the offender hard.

'How dare you strike my daughter?' came the angry voice of Malasha's mother who, happening to look out of the window, had seen what occurred. The two women started an argument in which some very unladylike language filled the air. Out came Malasha's father to see what was the matter. He joined the argument. Akulya's father then arrived on the scene and he started to let the others know what he thought.

Soon there was a crowd of parents, uncles and aunts of the two girls, all furious, all talking at the tops of their voices. Then someone went too far by using a word that he should not have. Sleeves were rolled up and the men prepared for a punch-up. Just as the first fist was raised someone said, 'Look at the girls.'

All eyes turned to Malasha and Akulya. They had found a sharp piece of stone and scratched a narrow channel through which the water was now flowing towards the lower village. They had thrown a piece of wood into the little stream and as it floated along they ran alongside, laughing and shouting.

'They've made up their quarrel and become friends again,' said a woman in surprise.

'And we were about to beat each other!' exclaimed a man. 'We should be ashamed of ourselves. These little girls have fallen out and forgiven each other in a few minutes, while we've been arguing for a quarter of an hour and were about to belt each other and start ill-feeling that might have lasted for the rest of our lives. If we must quarrel let's do it like children – quick arguments and quick forgiveness.'

Fists were lowered, smiles reappeared and the people of the village shook hands and went home in peace. Akulya and Malasha played on happily, not knowing at all what had been going on.

A Burglar Decides

In the darkened jeweller's shop the two burglars smiled at each other. Breaking in had been easy. Now all they had to do was pick up the most valuable pieces. The older man placed a slim torch on the glass counter. Next he produced a folded cloth string-top bag and carefully laid it out. He picked up the torch and flicked on the thin light. He directed its beam along the row of glittering brooches. The young man watched with eyes that gleamed with excitement.

His companion slid back the glass panel with the tips of his gloved fingers. His hand, led by the narrow band of light, moved skilfully along, picking up only the best. Suddenly the hand stopped. His ear had caught a sound – the sound of car brakes silently applied. He glided softly to the window. Then ' Jacks!' he hissed excitedly. ' We must've set off an alarm wired to the police station. Quick, up the stairs!'

The young man dashed up the stairs followed by his fellow-burglar. Up two, three flights they fled with pounding hearts and bursting lungs. At the top the young man flung open a wooden door and ran out on to a flat roof. The older man joined him a moment later, panting for breath. At that second they heard voices downstairs and the sound of heavy feet on the lower stairs.

' Separate!' cried the grey haired man. ' It's our best chance. You go that way.'

He turned and ran. The young man sprinted in the opposite direction. At the roof's edge a rusty fire-escape ran to the ground. Quickly he slid down, hardly waiting to put his feet on the rungs. Half-way down he heard a commotion below and saw running figures on the main road. He stopped on the ladder and scrambled on the narrow top of a wall. Slowly he inched his way along.

'Stop!' came a shout from close behind him, and the iron ladder rang as a policeman scurried after him. He sobbed with fear and heaved himself on to a long flat roof. He sped towards the other end as fast as he could. If he could reach the drainpipe there before the policeman caught him he would be safe, for he knew the little streets around the factory like the back of his hand.

He heard the thump of the policeman's feet behind him. He put on speed. Suddenly a wide glass skylight loomed up on the roof beneath his feet and he had to jump to avoid it. Only a few more yards to go, he thought joyfully. There was a startled shout and the crash of breaking glass behind him. Great, he thought, he's fallen through the skylight.

'Help, please!' came a moan from the broken window.

The young man stopped. He turned round. In the bright moonlight he could see the policeman's fingers clinging to the middle bar of the skylight. His body hung over the hundred-foot drop to the factory floor. The burglar turned away and strolled the last few steps to the corner drainpipe. No real need to hurry now, he thought. There was no-one else following him.

Then he stopped. It had just struck him that the policeman would fall if nobody helped him. He would certainly be seriously injured. He might be killed. I should save him, the youngster thought. But if I do, the rest'll come along in a minute and pinch me. He stood without moving for a few moments and then ran back to the policeman. Kneeling down he caught him by the wrists and began to pull with all his strength. As he held on he shouted, 'Over here! This way! Oi!' to attract attention. A short time later a hefty sergeant and two constables ran up and pulled their colleague to safety. As the wounded policeman lay panting on the roof he managed to gasp, 'Go easy on him, sarge. I'd be a goner without him.'

In court the police spoke up for the young burglar and he was given a much shorter term in prison than he would normally have received. He must have been sad about having to go inside, but he did get some comfort from the thought that he had given up his freedom to save another man's life.

Miss Martin's Mistake

Every Saturday morning Miss Martin used to make the breakfast for her brother and herself, tidy the cottage and change into her town clothes. Then she would take a five-pound note from the box in the drawer and set off for the station to do the weekly shopping. People used to say, " It's ten to nine. Miss Martin's on her way to catch the train." She took the nine o'clock to town and came back in the evening, her tall cane basket full up to the handle.

One morning in high summer she found herself sharing the carriage with an old lady who looked poor and pinched. Her coat was frayed at the cuffs and seemed too big for her. Probably a hand-me-down from some rich neighbour, thought Miss Martin. She noticed that the old lady was clutching a battered handbag, and wondered what pitiful odds and ends it held.

Soon the heat of the day and the soothing rhythm of the train made Miss Martin feel drowsy. She leaned her head against the corner of the carriage and closed her eyes. Within minutes she was asleep.

She woke up with a start, afraid that she had gone past her station, but a glance out of the window told her that they would not arrive in town for another few minutes. She took her handbag from the basket on the seat beside her. Opening it she took out her comb. Then her heart seemed to stop beating. She could not see her five-pound note. Anxiously she scrabbled among the bits and pieces at the bottom of the bag. It was not there. Wildly she searched her pockets. Of course it was not there either; she never put money in her pockets. Where could it have gone? she asked herself in great puzzlement.

Then her eye fell on the old lady opposite who was herself asleep, her head fallen forward on her breast and her breathing slow and deep. Could she have taken it? Could this poor old woman really have stooped to opening a stranger's handbag and stealing from it? What should she do? For a long time she turned over in her mind the different courses she could take. Then she made up her mind. Silently she stretched out her hand towards the old lady's handbag. Slowly, with shaking fingers, she undid the clasp. With great care she pulled back the flap. Then she leaned forward and peered in.

On top of the usual odds and ends lay a five-pound note. Miss Martin's eyes widened in surprise, for she had not fully believed what she suspected. Now what should she do? The police? No, she decided at once. She couldn't do that – not even to someone who had robbed her. Should she wake her and give her a red-hot telling-off? Then she smiled. She had a better idea. Gently she picked up the note between thumb and finger. She closed the handbag with the quietest of clicks. The old lady stirred in her sleep but did not wake up. Miss Martin tucked the note away in her bag just as the train pulled into her station. She rose, gathered her things, and took a last look at her sleeping companion. Then, smiling, she opened the carriage door and stepped on to the platform.

As soon as she got home that evening she said to her brother, 'You'll never guess what happened to me today.'

'I already know,' he said. 'You forgot to take your five-pound note with you. You left it on the table.' And he pointed to where the crisp note still lay.

'Oh, no!' said Miss Martin, as the shock of what she had done struck her.

The story ends there. We do not know if Miss Martin managed to get the fiver back to the old lady. But no doubt she learned not to think so badly of other people and never to act quickly without making sure that she was doing the right thing.

FOLK STORIES

Finn and the Scottish Giant

Finn was the biggest, roughest bully in the whole of Ireland. He was forever picking fights with smaller men and beating them without mercy. Soon he began to believe he was the best fighter in the world.

Then he heard about the Scottish giant. There came stories of a man as big as a windmill, with muscles like plum puddings and the temper of a bear. He could beat anyone, said the Scots, who were all scared stiff of him. Finn was angry when he heard these stories.

'Tough, is he?' said the big Irishman.

'I'll show him who's tough. I'll fix him.' With that he strode down to the beach and shouted across to Scotland – which is only thirty miles away – 'Scottish giant, I'm coming across to give you a good hiding. I'll take ship right away and I'll be there this afternoon.'

'Don't bother to come over here,' came a mighty roar from Scotland, 'I'll come over to you right now.' With that a mountain top came whizzing over and landed in the water half-way between the two countries, its tip sticking up. Then another great chunk of mountain seemed to fall out of the sky and into the water nearer to Ireland.

Finn turned pale. 'Glory be to God!' he gasped, 'he's using mountain-tops for stepping stones.' Like a flash he was up the

149

road and running home as fast as his legs would carry him.

'Hide me at once,' he shouted to his wife, Oonagh. 'There's a giant after me who can throw mountains.' Oonagh, who was a very sensible woman, said, 'Quick! Get into the baby's cradle.' She picked the baby out of the cradle and took it into the other room. Finn squeezed his big body into the cradle, pulled the little blankets up over his neck and huddled down. Oonagh swiftly put the baby's bonnet on his head.

There was a thunderous knock at the door and the house trembled. Oonagh opened the door and there stood the Scottish giant, his face purple with rage. 'Where is he?' he snarled.

'Not far away,' said Oonagh. 'Come in and you'll see him soon.' The giant came in and sat down.

'Would you like a glass of buttermilk and a scone while you're waiting?' asked Oonagh.

'Aye' growled the big Scot. Oonagh

went and fetched the meal and the giant tucked into it. Then he noticed the cradle in the corner. 'I see ye have a baby,' he said, rising and approaching the cradle. 'I'm verra fond of bairns.'

Finn crouched lower in his cramped quarters and stuck his face farther down into the blankets. To his horror the giant reached down and began to tickle his face. Then the big man put his fingers under Finn's chin. To his amazement he found his hand rasping along a whiskery jaw.

'Good heavens!' he gasped, 'this baby needs a shave. How old is he?'

'My baby is three months old,' said Oonagh, who was trying her best not to tell a lie.

'Three months,' said the Scot, 'and he already has a set of whiskers! I wouldn't be surprised if he had a couple of teeth.' And with that he put his finger in Finn's mouth. Finn bit as hard as he could, and the giant roared with pain.

'He has a full set!' he said with an air of wonder. 'Tell me, if your husband's three-month old son grows whiskers and a fine set of choppers what is the man himself like?'

'Finn is just a born fighter,' said Oonagh. 'He's really just a big clumsy boy who's always sorry afterwards and never fails to turn up at the funeral.'

'Funeral!' said the Scottish giant, turning pale. 'What do you mean – funeral?'

'Well,' said Oonagh, who had given up trying to stick to the truth, 'I told you he'd do anything for a fight. But he always goes too far and –' Oonagh took off an imaginary hat and held it over her heart, bowing her head like a mourner at a graveside.

For a moment the giant sat as if turned to stone. Then he was out the door like a greyhound and streaking for the safety of Scotland. Finn crawled out of the cradle, moaning with cramp.

'Now let that be a lesson to you,' said Oonagh. 'Remember that if you are forever beating people smaller than yourself there's always someone bigger who'll do the same to you. Besides, you're old enough to know better than to hit people weaker than you.'

And do you know, from that day on Finn changed his ways and became the gentlest soul in Ireland.

The Envious Athlete

Young Simon came in from the sunny Athens square and flung his toy spear in the corner. He sat down and moodily stared at his sandalled feet.

'What's wrong?' asked his mother.

'Nothing,' was the sulky reply.

'Come on,' said his mother.

The boy shook his head. 'It's Agenor,' he said. 'You remember – that big boy who came here once. He beats me into second place at everything – running, boxing, wrestling, reading. It's the same story every time; he's first, I'm second. I'd give my right arm just to beat him at something.'

'Let me tell you the story of the two athletes,' said his mother. 'Once upon a time, in this city, there were two splendid athletes. Each trained long and hard for the games. They looked equally fine runners – for it was running that each trained himself for – but one was just that little bit better than the other. Everyone looked forward to their races, for they always ended in excitingly close finishes. Half-way through the last lap they were usually neck and neck, elbows pistoning back and forth and breath coming in great gasps from their aching lungs. Then, inch by inch, the better man would draw away and cross the line a few yards ahead, to the wild applause of the crowd, who loved him. When he mounted the platform to receive the prize the roars of the spectators were deafening. When the second runner came forward they clapped politely.

'Now as time went by the unsuccessful athlete came to hate and envy the man who always beat him. He envied him his victories and, even more, the love the people had for him. They showed no affection for him, although he was almost as good as their favourite. He was pleased when the great athlete fell ill and could no longer run. Then, to his pleasure and the great grief of the citizens, the sick man died. The people of Athens loved him so much that they raised a fine marble statue of him in the middle of the city.

'Now at last the second runner came into his own. He won race after race. The spectators clapped politely. He was good, he heard them say, but not as good as the wonderful dead one. A mighty rage filled his heart. He took to standing in front of the statue glaring murderously at the smiling marble face of the man who had always beaten him. Even in death he had won.

'One night he stole out silently, carrying a hammer and chisel. He began to chip away at the base of the statue, stopping now and then to make sure that no-one was stirring. After some time he had cut through a corner of the grand figure. Another strong whack, he thought, will bring it down. He placed the chisel carefully and brought the hammer down with ringing force. A chunk of marble fell away, the statue tottered, teetered, and fell with a tremendous crash – right on top of him. They found him dead next morning – killed by envy, as someone said.'

Young Simon smiled. 'So I'm not to let envy kill me,' he said.

'Right,' said his mother. 'No matter how hard you try there may always be someone who is better. So don't waste your time wishing you had other people's talents.'

A Shocking Mistake

In olden times a knight named Folliculus lived in a tall castle with his wife and baby son. The baby was the apple of his eye and he spent long hours in the infant's bedroom playing and chatting with the chubby little fellow. He was also very fond of his dog, a lean swift greyhound which he always took with him on his hunting trips.

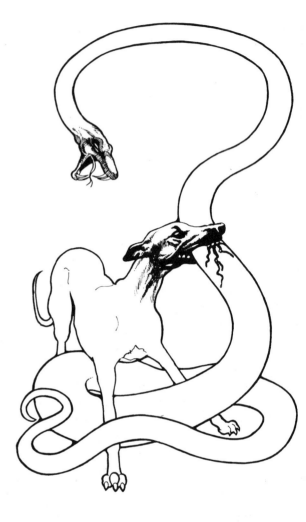

One day Folliculus was due to go to a tournament at the king's court. When he and his wife were ready to leave he took his greyhound up to the baby's room and made him sit by the little lad's cradle. 'Now you look after him while I'm gone,' he said. 'Don't let anything happen to my precious son.' He tucked the baby comfortably up and set off with his wife for the court.

The entertainment was fine that afternoon. Knights in full armour mounted on gaily dressed horses charged each other on the smooth lawns of the royal palace. Afterwards, in the great hall, a delicious feast was laid out on long tables while acrobats tumbled and minstrels sang comic songs to the sound of their stringed instruments. Folliculus enjoyed it all immensely and was truly sorry when the time came to go home.

When he arrived back at his castle his first action was to go to his baby's room, open the door quietly and tiptoe in. A terrible sight met his eyes. The cradle was overturned, the bedclothes lay in a heap on the floor and there was no sign of the baby. There was blood all over the floor. As the horrified father stared at this dreadful sight, his dog stood up and wagged his tail in greeting. His coat was matted with dried blood.

The knight's eyes opened wide with shock and unbelief. 'How could you have done this?' he whispered to the dog he had loved. Then, in a flash of bitter rage, he drew his sword and killed the creature with one stroke. Just then he saw a movement under the bedclothes on the floor. He whipped them up, and there lay his son unharmed and smiling. Beside him was a giant snake, dead and bearing on its body wounds clearly made by the teeth of the knight's faithful dog. At once Folliculus saw what had happened. The snake had attacked the baby. The dog had sprung to its defence. In the fight which followed the cradle was overturned, the snake killed and the dog wounded.

Folliculus covered his face with his hands and cried, 'What have I done? I have killed the loyal friend that saved my son. If only I had waited!' If only I had believed in him! If only . . .' and he wept for the terrible thing he had done.

From that day on the knight never let anger make him act in haste. He always waited till he was sure he knew all the facts before he acted, for he knew that in a sudden burst of rage he had done damage which could never be set right again.

The Sword of Damocles

Dionysius, King of Syracuse, became friendly with a man named Damocles. One day Damocles said to the king, 'You know, you must be the happiest man in this great city. You have what every man longs for – power and possessions. If you want something you have only to command it. What you decide can mean peace or war, life or death for the rest of us. As well as all this I'm told that your palace is the most comfortable and your food the most delicious of any king in the world. How happy you must be!'

The king smiled. 'You haven't been to any of my feasts, have you?' he asked. 'Why don't you come to the palace tomorrow night? I'll invite all the best people and you shall have the place of honour on my right-hand side. Then you'll be able to judge for yourself how wonderful life is for a king. Will you come?'

'I'd be delighted,' said Damocles, thrilled at the thought of dining at the king's side.

Next evening Damocles went to the palace. Dressed in his finest clothes he presented himself at the great oak door. A servant led him through a paved courtyard to the open door of the great dining-room. Damocles saw that the king and his guests were just about to take their places at the long table. Quickly handing his cloak to the attendant he took his place at the king's right hand. Dionysius leaned towards him and said, 'Well, what do you think?'

Damocles took his first good look around the king's dining-room. It was magnificently decorated with rich furnishings and priceless paintings. At the table were the noblest, richest and cleverest men in the city and its most beautiful women.

'It's marvellous,' said Damocles, and he meant it.

He looked up towards the finely carved ceiling. Then his eyes widened with shock and fear, for he saw a sword hanging by a single horse-hair from a beam, its point aimed directly at the top of his head. His first thought was to jump out of the way, but he stopped himself. He could not make a fool of himself before all these people. Then he thought of asking Dionysius if he could move his chair, but he could not bring himself to do it for fear of offending him. He had heard stories about the king's cruel streak. No, he thought, he would just have to sit through the meal with death hanging over him, held up by one hair from a horse's tail.

Damocles picked up his spoon and bent his head to drink his soup. He thought, 'If the hair breaks at this moment the sword will pierce the back of my neck.' Sweat broke out on his forehead. His soup might have been dishwater for all he knew. Every moment he expected to feel his skull being split and see his blood gushing over the white tablecloth.

The king told a joke at which everyone laughed. Damocles, his face stiff with terror, had to pretend that he was amused. It was agony. Some of the other guests spoke to him. He hardly knew what they were saying or how he answered them. He only knew that every time a servant opened a door the draught made the sword sway slightly. All he could do was pray that this ghastly dinner would come to an end.

It went on for two hours. Dish after dish of beautifully prepared food arrived at the table. Damocles ate what was set before him but he neither knew nor cared what it was or how it tasted. He sat numb with fear, now and then looking up to see the sharp sword pointing straight at his forehead.

At last Dionysius stood up. It was the signal for his guests to rise and go to another room to listen to music. Dazed with relief Damocles rose and moved out from under the sword. Dionysius took his arm and said, 'My poor friend, I'm sorry I made you suffer so much, but I really had to teach you a lesson. You see, you thought that being a king and living in a palace were so wonderful that I felt I had to show you that it means living with a sword hanging over you. I don't mean that I always have a sword over me, but I do have many cares. I have many enemies at home and abroad. I have sons who would dearly love my throne. The work of running my kingdom leaves no time for pleasure. My ministers plot against each other and against me. A king is a favourite target for assassins. Every meal may be poisoned. In short, I live among a thousand worries that the poorest beggar in my city never has to face. You spent two hours with a sword above your head. I spend my life like that. So never make the mistake again of thinking that power and wealth always bring happiness. Think yourself lucky that you are Damocles and not Dionysius.'

Damocles nodded. He had learned his lesson.

Aristippus and Dionysius

(Adapted from the *Apophthegms* of Bacon)

Another story about Dionysius tells of the time he met Aristippus. Now Aristippus was looked on as one of the cleverest men in the city. He was a thinker and teacher whose ideas were very much admired. He taught that the most important thing in life is to enjoy ourselves provided we do not hurt other people.

One day Aristippus came to the palace of Dionysius and asked if he could see the king. As it was the king's day for meeting the people Aristippus was quickly shown into the throne-room. He approached Dionysius and asked a favour of him. History does not tell us what the favour was but it is not important to the story.

The tyrant sat thinking for some moments, wondering whether to grant the request. Then Aristippus threw himself at the king's feet and begged him to be good to him. Dionysius, pleased to see one of the city's greatest men at his feet, gave Aristippus the favour he had asked for.

Outside the throne-room Aristippus was approached by a friend who had seen the whole incident. 'How could you do it?' said the friend angrily. 'How could you – our greatest thinker, respected the world over – bring yourself to fall at the feet of that boneheaded upstart?'

Aristippus answered mildly, 'It's not my fault that Dionysius carries his ears in his feet.'

'Carries his ears in his feet?' said the puzzled friend.

'I mean,' said the thinker, 'that if you stand upright he is likely to refuse you, but by kneeling to him you please him and he is more likely to say yes. It's as if he had his ears in his feet.'

'Ah.'

'Look,' said Aristippus, 'let me offer you a piece of advice. Get used to the idea that some time or other you'll have to ask nicely for something you want from someone you would like to strangle.'

'I'll remember,' said the friend thoughtfully.

The Indian Stonecutter

Once upon a time a poor stonecutter was breaking slates at the foot of an Indian mountain. Sweat gleamed on his face as he chip-chipped at the rock face. He stopped for a rest and sat on a flat stone. Looking up at the sky he saw a big dark cloud, all on its own, sailing across the blue. How wonderful, he thought, it must be to be a cloud; to float in the air far from the backbreaking drudgery of rock-bashing. Yes, he thought, I wish I were that cloud.

Now the rock he happened to be sitting on was a magic one which had the power to make the wishes of those who sat on it come true. In the twinkling of an eye the stonecutter became the cloud. How splendid it felt! There he was, floating free above the earth, laughing at the tiny humans scurrying about their work. Why, he thought, there's the king at the head of a procession of his nobles. What a stuck-up lot they look! I'll give them a shock. So he rained on them.

You should have seen the dignified march turn into a shambles as the magnificently dressed courtiers threw their cloaks over their heads and ran for cover. The cloud laughed till his sides ached. He was still laughing when the wind rose, grew stronger, and blew him away from the land and out over the sea.

'Hullo,' he said to himself, 'this isn't so good. I don't like being blown around

like this. I hope this wind dies down soon.'
But it did not; it got worse. Powerful gusts
hurled the poor cloud along at breakneck
speed and left him breathless and confused.
He found himself blown right around the
world and back to the mountain. As he
looked down on its peaceful bulk he said to
himself, ' How steady that mountain looks!
What a quiet, pleasant life it must lead. I
do wish I could become that mountain.'

And suddenly he was. What a relief it
was to rest in one place. He spent the whole
day just daydreaming in the sunshine and
loving his new-found peace. Nightfall
brought the first snag in his latest life with
a sharp frost around his head, or summit.
The cold made him shiver all night.

Next morning things were better. The rising sun warmed him and he set himself to enjoy a fine day. Suddenly he felt a sharp pain in his side. He winced with the shock. Then came another knife-like dig in the same spot, followed by another. He looked down at the place where he felt the pain. A stonecutter was chip-chipping at his side with a fine edged tool. He looked more closely at the man and—yes! It was himself in his human form.

How miserable I feel, thought the mountain. Here I am suffering, while the man down there is free of pain, healthy and, when his work is done, able to go home and live among his loved ones. What a fool I was to spend my time moaning about the sad life I led and wishing I was something different! I should've known that we must be content to be what we are, try to improve on what we are, and not waste our lives imitating others. If I could be that stonecutter again I would be a far more cheerful, thankful person than before. I do wish I were a human again.

Immediately he became a stonecutter once more. He never complained of his hard life after his strange adventure.

The Magic Mirror

Once upon a time there was a king who was the handsomest man in the land. His curly hair, bright eyes and tall, upright figure would have made all eyes turn to see him even if he had not been a king. Of course he knew he was goodlooking, for his mirror told him so every day, and he was pleased about it, but not bigheaded.

Now the king had a constant stream of visitors who came to see if the stories about his good looks were really true. There were politicians, nobles, rich merchants, neighbouring princes and just plain busybodies to be entertained. At every meal there was a crowded dining-hall and each night the palace lights burned long as the king feasted some important guest. He knew that many of his visitors came out of mere curiosity but he was too polite to turn anyone away. Besides, he got a kind of innocent pleasure out of being admired.

One day the king looked in his bedroom mirror and was shocked by what he saw. His bright eyes had grown dim and there were tiny wrinkles at their corners. His skin, which had always had a smooth, healthy shine, was yellowish. Worst of all, the clean-cut face had become puffy and looked as if it would soon show a double chin.

The unhappy man sent for all the best-known doctors and magicians in the land. He told them that he had lost his good looks and that it was up to them to see that he got them back. They must rack their brains to find the way to make their king the handsomest man in the country, and perhaps in the world. Well, they certainly tried their best. They produced pills, medicines, magic spells, special creams, mud plasters – you name it, they came up with it. The desperate man tried every one of them but do you think they did him one bit of good? No. It seemed to him that every day his mirror showed a face more lined, pale and plump than he had seen the day before.

At last he decided that doctors and magicians could not help him. He asked the prime minister to take him to the wisest man in the country. He was taken at once to the little house of an old man, who stroked his long grey beard as the king explained what the trouble was.

'I'll make your majesty handsome again,' said the old man, 'if you will do exactly as I tell you.'

'Anything, anything,' said the king.

'Your majesty will win back his good looks when he finds the magic mirror.'

'Magic mirror?' said the king. 'Never heard of it.'

'It lies somewhere up in the hills behind your palace,' said the old man. 'You must

look for and find it alone and on foot. When you see yourself in the magic mirror you'll be handsome again.'

'When do I start?' asked the king.

'Oh, there is one snag,' said the old man. 'The mirror can only be found early in the morning when the sun comes up. And if your majesty will take my advice he will not look in another mirror until he finds the one he's looking for in the hills.'

At sunrise the next morning the king was striding over the hills, his eyes darting here and there to catch sight of the magic mirror. He did not find it. He went to bed early that night to be fresh for his task the next morning. Again he had no success. He found it necessary to eat less than he had been used to, for roaming the hills just after dawn was no job for a man who had eaten too much. Morning after morning found him searching the windswept heights, but to no purpose. He saw no sign of what he so keenly longed to find.

One morning the wise old man was wakened by a noisy hammering at his door. It was the king, holding a small hand mirror. 'I've found it! I've found it!' he kept shouting. 'And it works!' The king looked proudly at the face that smiled back at him from the mirror. Gone were the lines, gone the plump, yellow appearance. His good looks were restored.

'I'm afraid,' said the old man, 'that I've played a little trick on your majesty. That is no magic mirror but the one I shave in every morning which I placed in the hills last night. You see, I knew that your loss of good looks was caused simply by too many big feasts and too many late nights. All you needed was plenty of fresh air, long walks and less rich food. My little story about the magic mirror was intended to get you those things. You know, every gift we have needs to be worked at and exercised, otherwise it goes bad. This applies to the gift of beauty as well as every other talent.'

The king laughed as he handed back the mirror. He was amused at the way he had been tricked but he made up his mind that he would not forget the lesson the old man had taught him.

Scheherezade

The Caliph or king, of Baghdad, was livid with rage. All the nobles of his court trembled as he glared furiously at them. 'I have found,' he said, 'that my wife was plotting with my enemies to kill me and put someone else on my throne. I have had her put to death together with the dogs who tried to bring me down. No woman is to be trusted. From this day on I shall marry a woman every day and have her put to death on the next. That will show what I think of women – greedy, selfish, treacherous bundles of trickery.'

The prime minister spoke up. 'Your majesty,' he said timidly, 'am I to understand that you intend to put to death one of our young women every day?'

'That is correct,' said the king sternly.

'But your majesty is still a young man,' said the prime minister, 'and may live for many years. If you kill one girl every day we shall soon have none left. Besides, do you think it fair to punish all women for the failings of one? And remember that you would be punishing not only our young women but their families. Think of the broken-hearted mothers, fathers and friends. Think also of the hatred you would stir up in every home in the city.'

'Silence!' shouted the king. 'Don't ever speak to me like that again. For your insolence I shall marry first that elder girl of yours – what's her name?'

'Scheherezade,' said the prime minister, pale with horror, for he dearly loved his daughter.

'Tell her to be ready for the wedding tomorrow,' ordered the king, and he stalked out of the room.

When the prime minister broke the terrible news to Scheherezade she took it calmly. All she asked was that she should be allowed to take her little sister Dunyashad to the palace for the wedding. Her father nodded, too overcome to speak.

Next morning the two girls went to the palace and the king and Scheherezade were married. There was a splendid wedding breakfast and the day was spent in singing, feasting and dancing. As darkness fell Scheherezade whispered to her sister, 'After supper ask me to tell a story.' Dunyashad nodded.

When the dishes had been cleared away the little girl did as she had been told. Scheherezade began a tale about a flying horse which was so exciting that the wedding guests sat silent, their eyes fixed on the storyteller, lost to all sense of the passing of time.

Suddenly the great gong boomed out twelve times. It was midnight – the time when, by the king's fixed rule, all members of the court must go to bed.

'I shall finish my story tomorrow night,' said the bride, 'in order not to keep anyone out of bed.' The king glared at her, for he had really intended to have her put to death the next morning. However, she had reached such an exciting point in her story that he thought he might as well let her live one more day to see how the tale ended. So he grunted, 'All right,' and the court went off to bed.

Next night after supper Scheherezade

continued her story. She was a wonderful teller of stories, and the king and all his nobles and their ladies listened with great attention. When she finished the tale of the flying horse everyone pressed her to tell another. So Scheherezade began the story of Sinbad the Sailor. Soon the nobles were listening, big-eyed, to the adventures of Sinbad. It came as a surprise to all to hear the gong boom twelve.

'Oh dear!' said Scheherezade, 'I shall have to finish tomorrow night.' The king was angry but he simply had to hear more about the remarkable sailor, so he said nothing and stumped up to bed. After all,

he thought, one more day doesn't matter.

Next night the queen carried on with her story and when she had finished they forced her to tell another. At midnight she was in the middle of the tale so she said she would finish the next night. The king unwillingly agreed.

This happened night after night. Scheherezade was careful to arrange that when the gong sounded she was at the most exciting part of the story, and the king would let her live next day to finish it. She played this trick for nearly three years. During the day she carried out her queenly duties in a way that made everyone love her. She was gentle to princes and beggars. She dressed modestly and gave money secretly to the poor of the city. She looked after her husband tenderly, calming his rages with her mild, soothing manner.

Scheherezade told her stories for one thousand and one nights. On the thousand and first, just as the midnight gong sounded, she finished her story. Everyone sat speechless, certain that the queen had made a terrible mistake. One noble whispered to his neighbour, 'Now she's for it. The king will have her head off tomorrow morning.' But the king heard him and, with a slow shake of his head, he said, 'No. I would as soon kill myself as my dear Scheherezade. I have learned from her that gentle ways are best. I have found out that trying to get our own back on people who have harmed us is wrong, and that punishing innocent people for the harm done by others is wicked. My only wish now is to live a good life with my clever Scheherezade.' And he did.

Damon and Phintias

When Dionysius, King of Syracuse, heard that there was a plot to remove him from his throne he was angry and afraid. He knew his people called him a tyrant, that is, a king who was cruel to his subjects. He realized that many of them would like to see him out of the way. But in spite of his hardness Dionysius thought he was a good king who did not deserve to be toppled from his throne.

He ordered his chief of police to seek out those who plotted against him and bring them to him in chains. Shortly afterwards the police chief returned with a young man, his hands chained behind his back. 'This is the plotter, your majesty,' he said with pride.

'Is this true?' asked the king. 'Did you plan to turn me off my throne?'

The young man raised his head proudly. 'Yes,' he said simply.

'Your name?' asked the king.

'Phintias,' said the prisoner.

'You shall die,' said the king. 'Guard!'

'Just a moment,' said Phintias. 'I know I must die. I expected to die if my plan failed, as it has. But I want to ask one last favour. I'd like to see my aged parents before I pass away. I also want to set my affairs in order – make my will, pay my debts, all that sort of thing. Now if you would free me for a short time – long enough to journey to my home and do these things – I should be grateful. You too would benefit, for your people would see that you can show mercy.'

The king roared with laughter. 'Do you really think I'd fall for a simple trick like that?' he said. 'Why, if I let you go I'd never see you again.'

'I swear I'd keep my word to return.'

The king stopped laughing and looked thoughtful. 'Come to think of it,' he said, 'I'd like to show my people that I can be merciful. I'll tell you what I'll do. I'll let you go home if you leave behind a friend. If you have not come back on the day appointed for your death your friend will die in your place. Now can you find such a person?'

'Send for my friend Damon,' said Phintias happily. The chief of police left and soon returned with a young man who at once agreed to stay as hostage for Phintias, though it was made clear to him that he would die if his friend failed to come back.

Phintias set out for his home village and Damon went to prison for safe keeping. His jailers had fine sport telling him that he had seen the last of Phintias. 'Would you come back if you were in his position?' they asked him. Damon smiled. 'He'll come,' was all he would say.

The days passed but there was no sign of the condemned man. The taunts of the jailers grew more mocking, but Damon showed no hint of worry. On the day before the execution date Dionysius decided to see how the young man was facing the thought of death next morning. He went to his cell and found Damon lying on his bed of straw, his face sad and miserable.

'Well,' said the king, 'I see you are feeling sorry for yourself. As well you might for trusting someone to give up his life instead of yours.'

'I'm not sorry for myself,' replied Damon, 'but for Phintias. He will return and die.'

'Don't fool yourself,' said the King. 'He may have meant to come back when he left, but once he got a taste of home cooking and thought of what was in store for him here he changed his mind fast enough, friendship or no friendship.'

At that moment there was a commotion outside the cell. The door opened and Phintias entered, followed by the jailer.

'My poor Damon,' said Phintias, 'I'm deeply sorry that you've had to put up with so much anxiety. I'd have been here much earlier but my ship went down in a storm.' Then, turning to Dionysius he said, "I am ready to die.'

The king looked at the two friends for a long time. 'Nobody is going to die,' he said. 'I have not seen friendship like this before and I'm not going to be the cause of breaking it. Phintias, I give you your freedom. There is something I now want to ask of you two. Let me be your friend. A king often does evil things through his friends, but if I had two like you I am sure I could become a better man and a better king.'

The young men agreed, and from that day on the trust that had existed between Damon and Phintias now grew among the three. History does not tell us if it made Dionysius a better king, but it would be nice to think that it did.

The Selfish Giant

(Adapted from a story by Oscar Wilde)

When the giant went off for a long visit to a friend the village children played in his garden every afternoon. It was a lovely garden surrounded by a high wall. In the spring peach trees broke out in pink blossoms and the grass was green and soft. The children loved to lie on the branches of the trees and gaze up at the pale blue sky.

One winter's day the giant came back and found the little ones spread out all over his garden. 'Get out of here!' he roared, 'and don't let me see any of you ever in my garden again.' The children took to their heels and were gone before you could say Jack Robinson.

Time passed. The children were now too frightened to go near the giant's garden. Instead, they played at the roadside, where the first flowers of spring soon poked their shy heads above the ground. But everyone noticed something very strange. In the giant's garden winter still ruled. Snow covered the bare branches and the grass stayed stiffly white with frost. Around the giant's house the icy wind howled, sending loose slates crashing on to the frozen ground. The villagers said it served him right and from then on they called him the Selfish Giant.

Spring changed into summer. The meadows were rich with the buzzing of bees. Gaily coloured butterflies flitted through the warm air. Everywhere the trees wore their summer clothing of green leaves. Did I say 'everywhere'? I should have said 'everywhere but the giant's garden', for inside those high walls the trees were bare and the earth rock-hard. It was a white and black scene without a flower to please the eye or a bird's song to charm the ear.

One morning the giant was wakened by what sounded like lovely music. It was only a bird singing outside his window but it had been so long since one visited his garden that it sounded like a great orchestra. The giant jumped from his bed and looked out of the window. An amazing sight met his eyes.

The children had stolen back into his garden and climbed the peach trees. There they were, boys and girls, swinging and

giggling among the branches. To welcome them back the trees had burst into blossom and the snow had disappeared, showing a soft carpet of bright green grass. Flowers of many colours filled the garden with the sweet scents of summer.

The giant's heart melted as he looked out. 'How selfish I've been,' he said. 'Spring wouldn't come here because I barred the children from my grounds. From now on they'll play here as much as they wish.'

Just then he saw a little boy crying bitterly under a tree inside the wall. He was too small to climb the tree. All around him it was still winter. He stood in the only patch of snow left. The giant hurried down the stairs and out into the garden to help him. When they saw him the children jumped quickly down from their perches and ran off. The garden turned white again.

The giant picked up the little fellow, who had not seen him come, and sat him on a branch. At once the tree put out its leaves and blossoms. The boy put his arms round the giant's neck and gave him a big kiss. The other children, who had been peeping round the gate, came running back and with them came the summer. Then the giant took a hammer and knocked down the wall.

'It's your garden now, children,' he said.

From that day on the young ones played without fear among the giant's peach trees and rosebushes, often with the big man himself tumbling and giggling as much as the smallest boy. He was no longer known as the Selfish Giant.

The Happy Prince

(Adapted from the story by Oscar Wilde)

In the autumn, when the weather turns cold, most of our birds set off for Africa to spend the winter in warmer lands. Once a swallow set out later than his friends and flew into an Italian city as night was falling. He spied a high statue in the city centre and decided to bed down for the night between the feet of the tall figure. Just as he was nodding off he felt a large drop of water fall on his wing. He thought it curious, for it was a cloudless night. Then another, and a third drop fell. He looked up, and to his surprise saw that the drops were tears falling from the eyes of the statue.

He flew up and had a close look. It was a splendid figure, covered from head to toe in gold leaf and with sparkling jewels for eyes. Another jewel glittered on the hilt of its sword.

'Who are you?' asked the puzzled swallow.

'I am the Happy Prince,' answered the statue. 'At least that's what people called me when I was alive. I used to rule over this city. I lived in a fine palace surrounded by a high wall. I had everything a man could want to make him contented, and I spent my life looking after my own pleasures. I never knew, and didn't want to know, how the poor of my city lived. When I died they

made the magnificent statue you see before you. But now I see how poor and miserable many of my people are. I can do nothing to help them. That is why I am crying.'

'How sad!' said the swallow.

'Perhaps you could help?' said the Happy Prince. 'In a room across the city I can see a woman sewing at a table. She is worn out but she must slave on to make a few coins in order to live. In the next room her little boy is tossing in a fever. That poor woman needs money to buy good food to make her child well. Will you pluck the jewel out of my sword hilt and take it to her?'

'Look here,' said the swallow, 'I need a good night's rest before setting out for Africa in the morning. I must get there before the frosts come.'

'Please!' begged the statue.

'Oh, all right,' said the swallow. 'But this is the last time, mind you.' He plucked the jewel from the sword and flew with it in his beak across the city. He winged in at the poor woman's window and quietly dropped the jewel on the table beside her thimble.

Next morning when he was about to set off for Africa the Happy Prince said, 'Please do one more thing for me. There is a poor young man trying to finish a play for the theatre in a miserable attic down by the river. He is cold and hungry and desperately needs money for food and a fire. Will you take one of the jewels that are my eyes and fly to him with it?'

The swallow grumbled a lot but, because he was good-natured, he did as he was asked. The young man thought that the jewel had been dropped in by someone who felt sorry for him and he carried on writing with new heart.

Next day the Happy Prince implored the swallow to stay one day longer. 'There is something I want you to do for me,' he said. 'Down in the square there is a little scrap of a girl. She sells matches for a living. She is crying, for she has just let all her matches fall in the gutter and they are all spoiled. When she gets home her father will beat her. Will you please pluck out my other eye-jewel and give it to her? Please.'

'But you'll be blind,' said the swallow.

'Never mind that,' said the statue. 'Will you do it?'

'Well, I should be away before this,' said the swallow, 'for the frosts can't be far off. But yes, I'll make this last trip.' So he plucked out the remaining jewel and flew to the street where the little match-girl was sobbing bitterly. He dropped the gleaming stone in her hand and she ran home laughing.

Next day the now blind Happy Prince asked the bird to peel off some of the gold leaf to give to the poor of the city. The swallow did so, for he was overcome with pity for the misery he had seen in his flights. Day after day he flew around with the glittering pieces in his beak bringing fresh hope to people who had nobody to turn to.

By now the Happy Prince was worried about the swallow, for the days were growing colder and the journey to the warm countries was a long one. He told him again and again it was time for him to fly off but the bird kept flying off with golden frag-ments for hungry people to exchange for bread.

Then one morning the swallow flew up and perched on the statue's shoulder. 'I have come to say goodbye,' he said.

'Good. It's about time you left for the warm air of Africa,' said the Happy Prince.

'No,' said the swallow, 'that's not what I mean. It's too late to go. I'm too cold and weak to fly. I meant that I feel death coming. So I must say goodbye.' And with that he fell dead at the statue's feet. Then the Happy Prince's leaden heart snapped in two.

When the councillors saw how shabby the statue had become without his gold covering they melted it down. The leaden heart, which they were surprised to find would not melt, was thrown on the dust-heap, where it lay beside the body of the little swallow.

Narcissus

The Greeks used to tell a story about a young man named Narcissus who was so beautiful that he fell in love with himself. The young women he met every day seemed so plain compared with the striking vision he saw when he looked at his reflection in the river that he could not force himself to become interested in any of them. Every day he would go and study his face in the slowly-gliding waters, marvelling at his glowing eyes, well-formed features and smooth skin. Then he would sigh aloud at the thought that he would never find anyone to love who had a face as perfect as his own. How sad, he thought, that the person I love lives only in the waters of the river, that I can never walk, talk, smile or laugh with him.

Now this idea – that he could not love anyone but himself – began to work on his mind. He could think of nothing or nobody but himself. He spent all his days at the riverside gazing at his reflection and sighing deeply. He grew ill with longing, quickly got worse and died.

Everyone was sad at the news of his death – even the gods. They thought it a shame that Narcissus should be lost for ever, so they put their heads together and came up with a fine idea. They brought him back to life in the shape of a flower, the one we now call the narcissus. Like the young man the flower is tall, straight and beautiful. Like him, too, it loves to stand by the side of the river admiring its face in the water.

'And that,' Greek mothers used to say, 'is how the narcissus got its name. But I didn't tell you that story just to amuse you. It shows that we must not become wrapped up in ourselves and that without contact with other people souls wither and die, as the body of Narcissus died.'

The Bar of Gold

Weeping John was a farm labourer. He was called Weeping John because he was always moaning about the hard life he led. 'Here I am,' he used to say, 'hardworking, honest and intelligent and yet I'm so poor I can hardly feed my wife and children. And if my health should fail and I shouldn't be able to work what would become of us all? Oh dear, life is full of worries.' And his blue eyes would fill up with tears.

Now much of John's trouble was of his own making. You see, farmers were unwilling to give him a job because he was so miserable that he depressed everybody he came in contact with. The farmers knew that they would get a better day's work from lighthearted labourers than from ones made gloomy by working alongside Weeping John.

One day the doctor invited John to his house. When he arrived there the doctor showed him a glass case in which was a shining yellow bar.

'This bar of gold was left to me by my father,' said he. 'He worked hard to buy it. When he left it to me I was as poor as you are now. It helped me to work harder and more cheerfully, for I now knew that if I ever hadn't enough to eat I could sell a little of the bar. Luckily I never had to touch it. I'm now well-off and no longer need the bar of gold. I want you to take it, Weeping John. If ever you find yourself in need sell it, or a part of it. I hope it does as much for you as it did for me.'

John took the gift, speechless with gratitude. He rushed home and told the story to his wife, who could hardly believe him. From that day John was a new man. He laughed and sang. He never worried about the future, for hadn't he enough gold to see him through any hard times? The farmers fell over themselves to have such a merry, hardworking fellow in their pay. He spent little, saved a lot and within three years had bought a little farm of his own. In ten years he had enlarged it to four times its size and was known as the richest farmer in the district. Not once during those years did he have to touch the bar of gold.

One summer evening John and his wife sat on their front porch watching the sun go down. A tattered stranger approached and asked for some food. John invited him in for supper. When they had finished the meal the beggar told them the story of his life – a tale of disasters he had not deserved.

'I'm going to do you a favour, my friend,' said John, rising and taking the yellow bar from the cupboard. 'Let me tell you the story of this gold bar.' He told of how he had received it from the doctor and what it had done for both of them. He finished by saying, 'Now I have no further need of it so I'm giving it to you. I hope it does as much for you as it did for me.'

The stranger took the gleaming metal in his hand. Then, with a smile, he said, 'I'm afraid you've been deceived, sir. This isn't gold. I know a good deal about these things and I tell you that this metal is too light to be gold.'

'Of course it's gold!' said John, taking the bar and rubbing it with his sleeve to show how brightly it shone. To his surprise the rubbing showed a few lines of writing cut into the metal. It read 'I am not gold, but if you believe I am you will have the courage to face life bravely.'

'I'm very sorry,' said John, astonished.

'Don't be sorry,' said the stranger, 'for I've learned a valuable truth from your story. From now on I'll believe in myself as you believed in your " gold " bar.'

Androcles and the Lion

Not long after Jesus was killed a Greek tailor named Androcles was travelling through a forest. He knew all about Jesus, for he was a Christian. As he walked along the forest path he wondered for the hundredth time at the bravery of Jesus in facing his dreadful death without fear. Androcles asked himself if he too could show such courage in the face of death. After all, he thought, it could happen at any time. The emperor's soldiers were hunting down Christians wherever they were to be found, and many of them met frightful ends on the cross or in the public games, where they were eaten by wild beasts.

Suddenly the mighty roar of a lion cut across Androcles's thoughts. It came from a thick clump of bushes just a few feet away. Now the tailor, though a timid little man, was extremely fond of animals, even the wildest and most dangerous. He had a fine understanding of them. Far from running away at the sound of the lion's roar he walked quietly up and parted the bushes.

'Just as I thought,' he said. 'The poor pussy is in pain.' In the bushes sat a fully-grown lion holding up a giant paw in which was stuck a large thorn.

'There now,' said Androcles, 'let me look at it. Androcles'll fix it.' He advanced slowly towards the powerful beast, which left off its piteous roaring to glare at the little man out of angry yellow eyes.

Androcles inched up to the lion and bent down. When he touched the big paw the creature pulled it away with a snarl. The tailor's shaking hand followed the paw, held it, and with a quick, expert tug drew out the thorn. The lion gave a last shout of pain, looked hard at Androcles, and ran off into the forest. Shaking his head with amusement and relief Androcles set off again on his journey.

Soon afterwards the little tailor was captured by the emperor's soldiers. He was recognized as a Christian and given a last chance to give up this new, strange belief. 'It's the arena for you if you don't, my lad,' said the captain of the guard. 'You know what that means.'

Androcles moaned, 'Yes, I know.' Already he could imagine himself in the middle of the sports stadium and see the wild animals bounding towards him, eager to sink their teeth and claws into his trembling flesh. It would be so easy to avoid it, to go free. All he had to do was declare he was no longer a Christian. He could walk away free. Yet, terrified though he was, he found he could not do it. He must try to act like Jesus, he thought. After all, that was what being a Christian meant.

So next day he knelt in the sand in the middle of the stadium while the big Roman crowd waited cheerfully to see the Christians torn to pieces. His hands were joined and he tried desperately to pray. All he could remember was the mocking voice of his jailer saying, 'We've got a lovely brute for you, mate. Caught him only yesterday. Wild as ever I saw a lion. We ain't fed him neither. You'll be his first meal. Not that he'll get much flesh off of a stringy little tich like you.'

Androcles dared to open his eyes for a moment and saw the hungry lion advancing on him. He closed them quickly and forced his shaking lips to mumble a prayer for the dying. The roar of the crowd grew louder and he knew the end must be near. Now he could feel the hot breath of the beast on his face.

Then, to his amazement, Androcles felt a rough tongue rasping along his cheek. It was licking him, he thought. He opened his eyes and found the great creature sitting in front of him. As the tailor stared, open-mouthed, the lion raised its paw, and Androcles suddenly understood. It was the lion he had helped in the forest. He put his arms around its shaggy mane and stroked its mighty head.

The emperor was so dumbfounded at what had happened that he pardoned Androcles on the spot. The tailor went free and lived a long, happy life. When the story got around most people commented on how lucky he had been.

'Lucky!' snorted one old Roman. 'He deserved his freedom. After all, he had guts enough to help the lion in the first place and he had guts enough to be willing to die for his beliefs. If someone like that doesn't deserve to live nobody does.'

King Midas

(Adapted from Ovid's *Metamorphoses*)

The Greeks used to tell the story of Midas, King of Phrygia, who was well-known for his fondness for money. Once he did a favour for Bacchus, the god of wine, who was so grateful that he told Midas he could have any gift he wanted.

'Anything I want?' asked Midas, his eyes glittering with greed.

'Certainly,' said the god.

'I wish that anything I touch may turn to gold,' said Midas. 'Can I have that wish?'

'If you're sure you really want it,' said Bacchus, looking strangely at the king.

'Oh, I do, I do,' said Midas eagerly.

'Very well,' said the god with a peculiar smile.

Midas could hardly wait to see if he really possessed the gift of changing everything he touched to gold. He picked up a stone and at once it became yellow. On his joyous way home he gathered ears of corn which at once changed into the precious metal. An apple became gold in his hand. When he reached his palace his first action was to turn the pale marble pillars to brightest amber.

Midas was overjoyed. He saw a wonderful future stretch before him. He would become the richest king in the world – the richest king who had ever lived. His palace would be made entirely of gold, yes, and everything in it. He would sleep in a bed of gold, between sheets of gold, resting

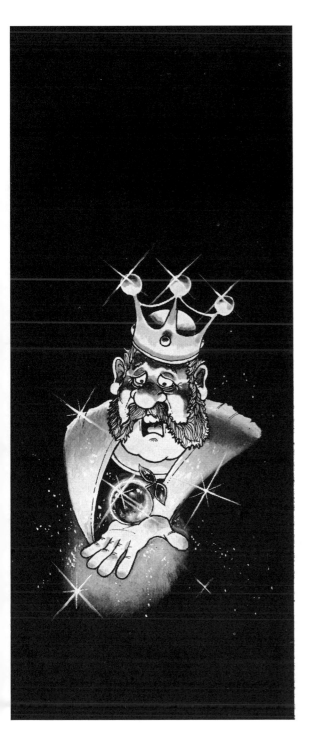

his head on a golden pillow. He would eat at a golden table from plates of gold.

He hurried to the table in the dining-hall and sat down. Laughingly he touched knives, spoons and plates to see them suddenly gleam with yellow light. He found that all this excitement had made him hungry. He picked up a piece of bread and put it in his mouth. His teeth crunched on a gold nugget. He speared a slice of meat on the end of a knife but immediately it touched his tongue it became gold. He spat it out. Then he tried drinking a glass of wine, but it became a golden liquid and nearly poisoned him.

Then the dreadful truth dawned on him. He was going to starve. This wonderful gift meant that he could not eat. What was the use, he thought, of being the richest man in the world if it meant starvation and death? Why, oh why had he been so greedy? Didn't every dunce in the land know that good health is far more important than riches? He must get rid of this golden touch. But would the god take back the gift once he had given it?

Bacchus laughed when Midas begged him to save his life. 'All right,' he said. 'Go and wash yourself in the river and the gift will go away.' Midas hurried off and did so. His golden touch vanished, and with it his greed for money.

The Bell of Atri

Far away and long ago there lived a king who decided at the beginning of his reign that any of his people who wished to make a complaint could do so as easily and quickly as possible. He ordered that in the centre of every town a bell should be hung. If anyone felt he had been wronged all he had to do was pull the bell-rope and, when the bell sounded, a judge would hurry over from the law-courts and look into the matter.

In the old town of Atri this idea worked splendidly. Soon no man was willing to beat or cheat another for fear of being shown up in the market-place. Shopkeepers stopped overcharging for their goods. Sharp-tongued ladies were more careful about whom they criticized. Workmen took their pay home on a Friday night instead of heading straight for the pub. Wives cut down on their nagging and husbands gave up beating their wives. Some of the town's worst rascals left the town altogether, for they were too steeped in villainy to change and they could not face the judge every day.

So well-behaved did the people of Atri become that the bell rang out less and less as time went on. Finally it stopped ringing at all. Dust gathered on the top. The rope rotted and broke. Someone twisted a few strands of straw and tied them to the frayed end so that the bell might still be rung.

Years passed. The townspeople were

by now proud of their dusty, moss-covered bell. Its silence meant that they lived in peace. Its mouldy appearance assured them that no-one was being wronged.

Then one terrible summer's day the great bell's iron tongue rang out its angry message. Clang! clang! it sounded on the warm air. The people of Atri looked at each other in amazement. Then they rushed out of doors and into the market-place to see who had rung the bell. A judge pushed his way through the crowd asking, 'Who did it? Who did it?' The townspeople stepped back to let him through. When he reached the rope he stopped and stared, astonished.

An old horse was hungrily chewing the straw rope. With every tug the bell pealed loudly. The judge looked the animal over. Its mane was tangled and filthy. Its bones showed through the skin. From the wild glint in its eyes the judge could tell that it had not eaten for a long time.

'Who owns this poor creature?' he shouted.

'Lord Flint, sir,' answered an old man. 'That horse used to be a fine animal that carried its master proudly, but now that it's old and weak Lord Flint has thrown the poor thing out of his stables to look after itself.'

'Someone go and tell Lord Flint that I should like to see him at once,' cried the judge, his face red with anger.

A boy ran off and soon returned with Lord Flint. The judge told him he ought to be ashamed of himself. His horse, he said, had given him loyal service in its youth and deserved at least enough to eat in its old age. Neglect of animals was a special kind of cruelty. He must now take the starving creature home and see that it was properly looked after. Lord Flint left with his horse, looking flushed with shame.

Once again the bell of Atri was silent. The townspeople were now able to say that even a horse could have his wrongs righted in Atri.

A Son of Adam

A farm labourer was digging a trench on a hot summer day. Sweat poured down his face and neck in tiny rivers. He stopped, leaned on his spade, wiped his wet forehead and said aloud to himself, 'What a miserable life this is! And to think that it's all the fault of that stupid Adam.'

'What's that?' said a voice behind him. 'What's that about Adam?'

The farm worker turned round and saw it was the farmer for whom he was working. 'Oh, hello master,' he said. 'I was just saying what a pity it was that Adam ate the apple from the forbidden tree. You know the old story – that we would all live happily ever after if that first man had minded his own business. I wouldn't be working like a horse today. I'd be sitting contented in a Garden of Eden.'

The farmer laughed. 'Poor Adam gets blamed for a lot of things,' he said. 'Besides, how do you know you wouldn't have done the same thing if you had been in his place?'

'Because I have more sense,' answered the farm labourer. 'Because if I'm told to do something and say I'll do it, I do it.'

'How right you are!' said the farmer. 'Well, I must be off to see to the cows. Will you come up to my house and have dinner with me tonight?'

'Sure,' replied the other, brightening

up at the thought of a big meal after his hard day's toil.

That evening he washed and shaved. Then he strolled over to the farmer's house. His master showed him into the dining-room where the table was laden with the most tempting dishes. On an oval blue plate in the centre of the table rested a plump turkey, cooked to brown perfection. Around it, on smaller dishes, were fruits, meats, jellies and cream.

'I must leave you for a little while,' said the farmer, 'but don't wait for me. Start right away. Eat whatever you like – oh, with one exception; don't touch what's in that little covered dish, please. Don't even pick up the top dish.'

'Of course not,' replied the labourer.

The farmer went out and the hungry man tucked into his meal. First he carved himself a generous slice of turkey and ate it with vegetables and gravy. Then he polished off several jellies smothered in thick cream. He finished the meal with two cups of tea and a number of sweet biscuits. Then he sat back and smacked his lips in a thoroughly contented way.

His eye fell on the covered dish. He wondered what it could be. He thought how strange it was that the farmer should forbid him to uncover it. Perhaps he was afraid that his visitor would steal it. What could it be? Could it be a kind of food, or fruit, so delicious that the farmer wanted it for himself alone. Suddenly he ached to know what it was – what it tasted like. His trembling hand reached out and lifted the top dish.

Out popped a mouse, ran across the tablecloth, and jumped on to the floor. 'Good heavens!' said the farm worker, 'if I don't catch it and put it back under the plate master'll know I looked under the dish.' He dived at the terrified mouse. But it was too quick for him and sprinted down the nearest hole.

In a panic the poor man put the top dish back in its place and miserably wondered what to do. At that moment the farmer came in. His first action was to pick up the top dish.

'Well, well,' he said. 'So you fell for my little trick. Perhaps it was a bit cruel, but I did want to teach you that there's no use in blaming poor old Adam for our own faults. You do see that you did exactly the same thing that Adam is said to have done.' The farm worker smiled in a sad sort of way. He decided that from then on he would not name other people as the cause of the misfortunes which he himself had brought about.

Pandora's Box

One of the oldest stories in the world tells of the day that Hermes, the messenger of the gods, brought the first woman down to earth. He took her to the brothers Prometheus and Epimetheus and said, ' Here is a present from Zeus, the king of the gods. He had her made by the god of fire, who is a wonderful artist, and all the other gods have given her their own special gifts. Her name is Pandora. Zeus hopes she will gladden your lives.'

Epimetheus was overcome with admiration for the beautiful creature who stood before him shyly holding a strangely carved wooden box. ' We're delighted to have her,' he said, ' and we'll always look after her.'

' Not me!' said his brother Prometheus angrily. ' There's a catch here somewhere. Zeus hates us. He hates all who live on earth. He's never forgiven me for stealing fire from his hearth and giving it to men. Remember that he chained me to a rock and let an eagle eat my liver until Heracles killed the bird and set me free. Don't have anything to do with this woman, Epimetheus. She's another of Zeus's tricks.'

But his brother had fallen in love with Pandora and would not listen. Epimetheus asked her if she would be his wife and she smilingly agreed. As they set off for his house Epimetheus asked, ' What's in the box?'

' I don't know,' said Pandora. ' When Zeus sent me down he gave it to me and told me to keep it but never to open it. If I did, he said, all sorts of trouble would result.'

Epimetheus looked serious. ' We'd better do as he said. I'll put it on the shelf out of harm's way,' he said. He did this, and the young couple set about preparing the house for their life together.

Epimetheus quickly found that Pandora had all the gifts the god had claimed for her. She was patient, hardworking, gentle, generous and humorous. It was true that her coming had brightened his life. However, he could see that she was not quite perfect; he noticed a streak of curiosity in her nature – a desire to know everything – that sometimes made him feel uneasy. Still, this small fault seemed unimportant compared with her many good points.

As for Pandora, she loved being the wife of Epimetheus and the only woman on earth. She was thoroughly satisfied with life. Only one little problem nagged at her. As time went on she became more and more curious about what was in the box. What could it be? She spent hours wondering. As the days went by the box seemed to become more attractive. When Pandora found herself in the house alone she felt her feet lead her to the shelf where the box sat. It was made of polished wood and the lid was tied down with a golden cord, queerly twisted. Often she looked down at the tempting thing and felt her fingers straying towards the plaited yellow cord. But always she remembered the warning of Zeus and tore herself away from the box.

One day when Epimetheus was out Pandora found herself once again looking at the mysterious box. Almost without her knowing it her fingers stroked the cord. It seemed to untwist itself before her shocked eyes. She gave a quick tug and it was out of the clasp before she could stop it. All she had to do now was lift the lid. Pandora told herself not to do it. It was wrong, she said. But what was inside it? What could possibly be inside a small box that could do any great harm? She opened the box.

Out flew a swarm of little winged demons with long stings who buzzed angrily around Pandora's head and then streamed out of the open window. Wildly she wondered what they could be. She soon knew. They were the Troubles, spirits which brought pain, worry and sickness into a world which knew nothing of these things. However, there was also one good spirit – Hope – which helped the human race to put up with all the others.

When Prometheus heard the news he was deeply enraged. 'I told you so,' he said bitterly to his brother. 'I warned you. Zeus made this woman charming so that you would love her and keep her, but he gave her curiosity, knowing that it would make her open the box. Now mankind will have to put up with all these miseries.'

So the Greeks blamed Pandora for all the troubles of life as the Hebrews had blamed Eve. They often told their children this story to impress on them how unhealthy curiosity might lead to disaster.

Lazy Jack

Jack lived with his mother, a poor widow who made a bare living by spinning wool. He never lifted a finger to help her in the house or out of it. If he was not to be found curled up in bed he was sitting sunning himself in a rocking-chair in front of the house. Everyone called him Lazy Jack.

One day his mother lost all patience with him. 'Get out and find a job this minute,' she shouted, 'and if you can't get one don't come back here. I'm sick, sore and tired of your bone-idleness. I mean it, now. Find a job or find another home.' And she banged the door behind him.

Lazy Jack knew she meant what she said, so he went and got a day's work from a neighbouring farmer. He was given a pound note for his labour and he fingered it with pleasure on the way home. As he was crossing a bridge the note fluttered out of his hands and down into the river. It quickly sank in the muddy waters.

His mother was most annoyed. 'You should have put it in your pocket,' she said.

'I'll do that next time,' said Lazy Jack.

The next day Jack did another day's work for a cattle-dealer who gave him a jar of milk as payment. The young man put it in his jacket pocket. When he got home the milk had long before spilled all over his jacket and trousers. His mother shook her head in anger. 'You should have carried it on your head,' she said.

'I'll do so next time,' said Lazy Jack.

Next day Jack got a job with another farmer. At the end of the day the man gave him a big round cheese for helping him. Jack set off for home with the cheese carefully balanced on his head. Now it was a sunny day in the middle of summer. When Lazy Jack got home what do you think had happened to the cheese? It had melted and run down his hair and neck. 'You silly boy!' shouted his mother. 'You should have carried the thing in your hands.'

'I'll do that next time,' promised Jack.

Next day he went to help out in the baker's. When he had finished the baker gave him a cat instead of the money he had hoped for. Jack held the cat in his hands as he set off for home. Now cats don't like being gripped in people's hands, and this one soon let Jack know that. She bit and scratched so much that he had to let her go. She ran off in the direction of the baker's. The young man's mother was more furious than ever. 'You should have tied a string around it and pulled it after you, you brainless clown!' she hissed.

'I'll do that next time,' said Lazy Jack.

His next job was with a butcher, who gave him a piece of steak as payment. Sure enough he tied a piece of string around it and pulled it all the way home. When he got there the meat was filthy. His mother said, 'How did I come to bring up such an empty-headed idiot? You should have carried it on your shoulder.'

'I'll do that next time,' said Jack.

Next day he did a day's work for a horse-dealer. This man gave him a donkey for his wages. Jack got the beast up on to his back after a desperate struggle and staggered off in the direction of his home.

Soon he came to a large house. At the upper window sat a young and beautiful girl. Her face showed her unhappiness, for she was deaf and dumb. She had never laughed in all her young life, and the doctors had told her rich father that she would never be cured until someone made her burst out laughing. Many young men had tried to make her laugh, for her father had promised her in marriage to the man who cured her, but none had succeeded.

This then was the sad young woman who sat looking along the high road. Sud-denly she sat up. Round the corner came what looked like a young man carrying a donkey. It can't be true, she thought to herself. Donkeys carry men; men don't carry donkeys. As she watched, the figures came nearer and she saw that it really was a man carrying a donkey and stagger-ing from one side of the road to the other. A look of astonishment crossed the girl's face, followed by an enormous smile. Then she threw back her head and howled with laughter. At once her parents rushed in, overjoyed to find her cured. Their next step

was to bring in Lazy Jack, who immediately took to her. He was delighted to find that her father had promised to give her in marriage to the man who restored her speech and hearing.

The young couple had a glorious wedding and went to live in a large house owned by the bride's father. Lazy Jack brought his mother to live with them and, thanks to the riches of his father-in-law, he became a gentleman and never had to do a stroke of work again.

I wonder if you are glad that everything worked out so well in the end for Lazy Jack. Or perhaps you feel that an idle dunce like Jack did not deserve a beautiful bride and a rich father-in-law.

The Prince and the Blacksmith's Daughter

One day a prince rode out of his palace and went to the field where the blacksmith's daughter was digging potatoes. 'I want you to marry me,' he said, 'and come to live in my castle.'

The girl said, 'Yes I will, on one condition. If you ever scoff at me for being only a blacksmith's daughter I'll leave your castle for ever. When I leave I'll take with me all I can carry on my back over your drawbridge in three journeys.'

'Agreed,' said the delighted prince. 'But there'll be no need for you to leave – I promise. I'll make you happy.'

'Maybe. But remember you have a very bad temper which leads you to say things you don't really mean. Remember too how proud you are of your royal family.'

The prince only laughed and took his bride off to the castle where they were married next day with great feasting. They settled down and became wonderfully happy in the princess's new home, and when they had a little baby son it seemed as if life had nothing more to give them.

One day the prince and his wife were seated on their thrones in the judgment hall listening to people who had come with requests or to have their disputes settled. One of them was a monk who asked the prince if his monastery might have the apples left over from the prince's orchard when they were gathered in the autumn. The prince, who was feeling rather cross that day, said, 'You monks are always asking for something or other.'

'I'm not asking for your apples on behalf of us monks,' was the reply, 'but for the poor people we can help by selling those apples in the market. We don't want them for ourselves, but for our Master.' And the monk raised his eyes towards Heaven.

The princess, who thought her husband was being rude, said jokingly to the monk, 'Tell your Master to come and ask nicely for the apples and perhaps He'll get them.' At this the prince lost his temper and roared, 'Who do you think you're talking to? Remember that my ancestors have sat on this throne for the last thousand years deciding these things while yours have been making shoes for horses.'

He stopped, shocked at what he had said, but it was too late. The princess rose and ordered the guard to let down the drawbridge. She went to her room and filled a sack with the most precious jewels the prince owned. She walked over the drawbridge to the other side and put down the sack. The prince only smiled, for he was very rich. She came back and picked up her son, swung him up on her back and crossed the drawbridge. The prince did not smile this time. Coming back for the third time she said, 'Now it's your turn.' She took him by the hands, painfully hauled him on to her back and staggered over to the other side.

They went to live in the blacksmith's house and – can you believe it? – they were happier than they had been in the castle and the prince rarely lost his temper again.